ANTALYA
Museum Guide

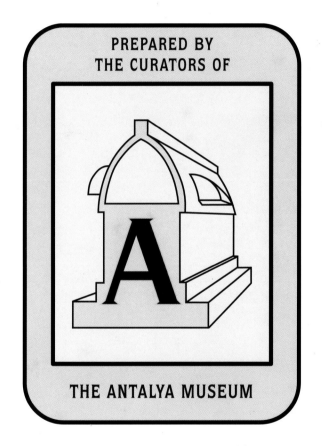

PREPARED BY
THE CURATORS OF

A

THE ANTALYA MUSEUM

ISBN 975-17-1640-3

Antalya Museum Publication II
June 1996

HOW TO GET TO THE ANTALYA MUSEUM

FROM : The dolmuş (shared taxi) stand across from the Atatürk Monument at the city center,
TAKE : A dolmuş (shared taxi) to:
      Meteoroloji İstasyonu (the Meteorological Station), or
      Bahçeli, or
      Liman (Harbor).
The Museum is on the right hand side, before the road turns to the Konyaaltı Beaches.

SUMMER SCHEDULE :
OPEN DAILY (except on Mondays)   9:30 a.m. - 6:30 p.m.
OTHER SEASONS :
OPEN DAILY (except on Mondays)   8:30 a.m. - 12:00 noon
                                    1:30 p.m. - 5:30 p.m.

MUSEUM FACILITIES :
A small refreshment area - Open-air galleries - Small amphitheatre - A yard with corners to relax in while admiring a magnificent view.
Guidebooks, postcards, souvenirs and slides on sale at the ticket window.
Entrance fee 270,000.- TL. (for 1996)

Visitors are free to take pictures. For the use is necessary of tripods authorization from the museum management.

The rest rooms are to the right of the main entrance of the museum.

No smoking inside the museum.

THIS GUIDE BOOK HAS COMPLIED FOR THE MUSEUM
UNDER THE CONTRIBUTION OF THE MUSEUM DIRECTOR

Metin PEHLİVANER

AND MUSEUM CURATORS

İ. Akan ATİLA - Sabri AYDAL - Ferhan BÜYÜKYÖRÜK - Ünal ÇINAR - Nermin ÇOLAK
Mustafa DEMİREL - Ünal DEMİRER - Hamdi KODAN - Selahattin KOR - Edip ÖZGÜR
Cihan TİBET - Ahmet TOPBAŞ - İlhan ÜNLÜSOY - Azize YENER

- Text and Art layout by   : İ. Akan ATİLA - M. Edip ÖZGÜR
- Translation by   : Niğar ALEMDAR - Dr .Üner BEKÖZ
- Photography by   : İ. OKMAN, T. BİRGİLİ, T. ÇAKAR, O. ATVUR, İ.A. ATİLA
- Printed by   : DÖNMEZ OFFSET - MÜZE ESERLERİ TURİSTİK YAYINLARI - ANKARA
                                  G.M.K. Bl. 77/E - 06570 Maltepe - Ankara • (312) 229 7961 - (312) 229 2569

This book is dedicated to the late S. Fikri ERTEN, the founder of the Antalya Museum, and to all others who have contributed to making the Museum what it is.

CHRONOLOGY

Palaeolithic Period ➯ 8000 B.C.

Neolithic Period ➯ 8000-5500 B.C.

Chalcolithic Period ➯ 5500-3000 B.C.

Early Bronze Ages ➯ 3000-2000 B.C..

Middle - Late Bronze Ages ➯ 2000-1200 B.C.

New Hittite Kingdoms ➯ 1200-700 B.C.

Urartian Kingdom ➯ 900-600 B.C.

Phrygian Kingdom ➯ 700-550 B.C.

Lydian Kingdom ➯ 700-550 B.C.

Hellenistic Period ➯ 330-30 B.C.

Roman Period ➯ 30 B.C.-330 A.D

Early Christian/Byzantine Period ➯ 330-1453 A.D.

Seljuk Period ➯ 1071-1300 A.D.

Ottoman Period ➯ 1299-1923 (Proclamation of the Turkish Republic)

CONTENTS

INTRODUCTION

Not alone the prosperity from the fertile soil of Anatolia, having fed millions of souls of uncountable civilizations, but, history also does erupt. Anatolia ironically becomes the land to those from everywhere on earth when geographical facts sustain natural beauties of the divergence unlike anywhere known.

This, consequently, innervates what Turkey is now with its bound role: an unabridged mosaic from the east to the west.

A mosaic tissue with far distances, on one side you are likely to hear a caveman's struggle to turn a piece of stone into an axe while on the other side the anxious whisper and fall of a bunch of spica on a swift sickle behind the abode walls.

It really is not surprising to face Virgin and Child figures right in front while watching amazingly enormous marble blocks resting overhead as though they float in the air. Further one is to become very much fervent under domes of the mosques wondering how possible to cover such large area under a dome.

The province of Antalya is endowed with the richest natural and historic treasures of Turkey. This large province includes a long coastal strip on the Mediterranean and fertile lands inland. It also includes the ancient regions of Lycia, Pamphylia, Cilicia, and Pisidia which form the most interesting archeological sites where uninterrupted history from the traces of the earliest man to the present can be found.

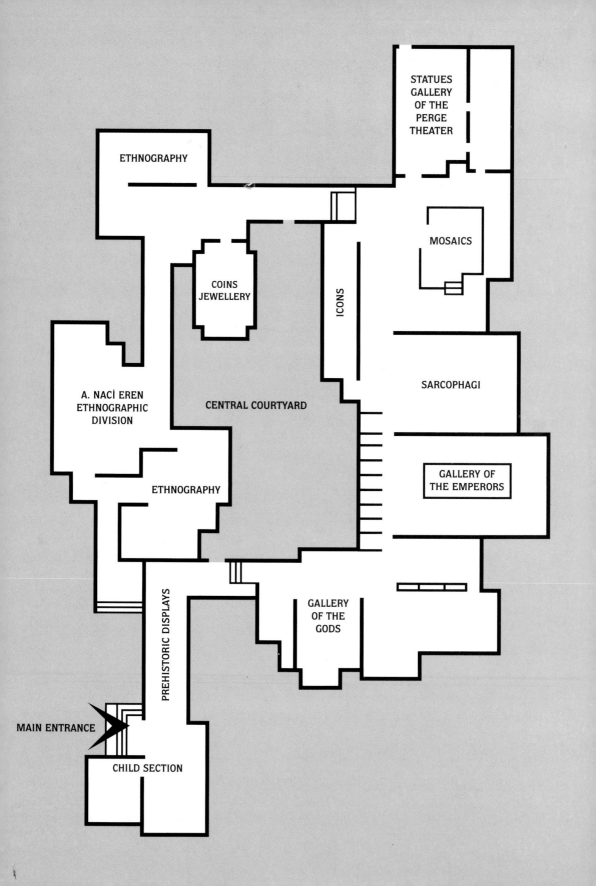

STATUES
GALLERY
OF THE
PERGE
THEATER

ETHNOGRAPHY

MOSAICS

COINS
JEWELLERY

ICONS

A. NACİ EREN
ETHNOGRAPHIC
DIVISION

CENTRAL COURTYARD

SARCOPHAGI

ETHNOGRAPHY

GALLERY OF
THE EMPERORS

PREHISTORIC DISPLAYS

GALLERY
OF THE
GODS

MAIN ENTRANCE

CHILD SECTION

Regarding all these, Antalya region is a phenomenal history and archaeology school for our profound world.

Work goes on. While on one side The University of Pennsylvania team uncover pithos burials (earthenware graves) of the first Bronze Age, on the other, either Vienna University specialists recover the Heroon, tomb of a Lycian King, Perikles or Tübingen University with a complete different curiosity and Ankara University with indefatigable effort, overwhelmingly wondering how many more thousands of years will they be able to go down into the darkness of first human ages.

Converting this massive action into figures, merely in the summer time of 1995 in Antalya region, 15 archaeology teams emerged worked on the dense and chronological history of a fertile landscape.

The invaluable concrete evidence attesting to the region's history is displayed at the Antalya Museum which ranks third among Turkey's historical and archeological museums after the Istanbul and Ankara Museums.

The founding of the Antalya Museum dates back to the dark years following World War I. Those artifacts saved by a teacher, Süleyman Fikri,from the looting of the occupying forces, form the basis of the museum.

Until 1957 the Alaaddin Mosque served as the museum building. The Yivli Mosque was the next home of the museum until 1972. The present museum building was completed in 1972 and has become the final and true home of the artifacts. However, due to the increasing yields of recent excavations this new domicile, too, became inadequate; the museum was closed for rearrangement in 1982 for three years.

The Antalya Museum which re-opened its doors in April 1985 , today covers an area of 30,000 square meters with fourteen galleries, open-air galleries, and a wide yard. The latest addition to the museum is Hall Number Three which was opened in 1988. Also known as the Rescue Excavations Hall, Hall Number Three is where the sensational Phrygian finds are displayed. These artifacts on display come from the tumuli of the Elmalı-Bayındır villages excavated by the archaeologists of the Antalya Museum.

Within the same exhibition area, pottery samples from back in 5th Century BC. of Karaçallı Necropolis are other findings of the Museum in a separate rescue excavation.

The hall where findings from the ancient theatre of Perge, uncovered by Prof.Dr. Jale İNAN, are exhibited, is, undoubtedly, the newest and the most exhilarating section of the Antalya Museum. This is the unique hall amongst the counterparts in the whole world by mirroring the outstanding ancient theatre ornamentation samples of friezes, statues,etc. spurting out from the invaluable artistic understanding of the ancient life.

Approximately five thousand archeological pieces, all belonging to the region,are displayed mostly chronogically.In some places the finds are exhibited according to subject matter. In other words, visiting the Antalya Museum is taking a trip into the history of Anatolia - a trip that takes one from the first flintstone tool of man to a recently woven carpet by local nomads.

On the two walls of the entrance hall that comes before the main halls of the museum,there are ceramic panels. The panel on the right depicts the Yivli Mosque and typical white-washed Turkish homes as well as the 19th century appearance of the inner portion of the castle of Antalya. The panel on the left, however, displays a map of the ancient cities as well as the map of the present province. The plaque to the left of the main entrance is an award from the Council of Europe recognizing the Antalya Museum as The Museum of the Year at their 1988 meeting in Delphi.

This guide to the museum was prepared with the intent of facilitating the understanding of the history of Asia Minor, especially the history of the region, its archaeology and art... Have a nice visit.

Metin PEHLİVANER
Director of the
Antalya Museum

EUROPEAN
MUSEUM OF THE YEAR
AWARD

Special Commendation 1988

The Committee would like to take this opportunity of expressing its
appreciation of the achievements of

Antalya Museum, Antalya, Turkey

and has great pleasure in making this Presentation as a
permanent record of its esteem.

Richard Hoggart

RICHARD HOGGART
Chairman

THE CHILDREN'S ROOM (Hall I)

The first hall to the right of the entrance to the museum was designed for children in 1985, the Children's Year, and was dedicated to the children of the world. The aim with this foremost section is to transmit the basic idea to the children that the archaeology and history of the region they live in are very spectacular for their personal education and social well being.

Baked clay toys in the display cases not only remind that one begins life by playing, but also recalls to mind the value of games and playing in one's life. These toys consist mainly of small carts or different kinds of animal figurines.

On the walls the copies of tablets written in the cuneiform script exemplify the Sumerian alphabet. Just like today, even in antiquity education started with the teaching of the alphabet.

Panels describing the construction techniques of the monuments are also displayed on the walls. To promote interest in museums and antiquities, the workshop stands include the tools necessary for the construction and the repair of ancient artifacts.

The ethnographical exhibition on the floor of the section samples the life in a small town at the beginning of the century in Anatolia. The scene is based on the real, today vanishing, structures of the essential ingredients of daily life, like a blacksmith, a potter or a coppersmith etc. modelling the design of the workbenches with then used tools as well as modelling the characteristics of life.

From time to time, the award-winning artistic works of school children are displayed also in this hall.

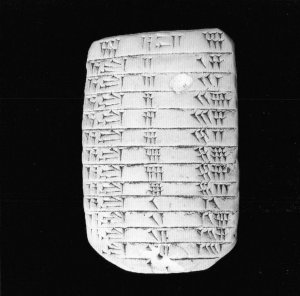

Toy
Baked clay

Copy of a Sumerian Cuneiform Tablet:
multiplication tablets
Second millennium B.C.

14

The Ethnografical exhibition of the Children's Room.

HALL OF NATURAL HISTORY AND PREHISTORY (Hall II)

The second hall of the Museum, The Hall of Natural History and Prehistory begins with three show-cases containing various fossils from different geological periods. By the ingredients in there show cases it is aimed to suggest the period, teeming with life, long before-millions of years-the man thrived.

In the hall of natural history and prehistory traces exhibited are all from five main excavations of the region. These are, in order of chronology;

1 - Karain Cave

2 - Bademağacı mound

3 - Hacılar

4 - Elmalı - Semayük and

5 - Gökhöyük excavations.

The Karain Cave near Village of Yağca and 30 km. North-West of Antalya is the source of the majority of the artifacts next to Natural history displays. The Karain Cave was first excavated by Professor I.Kılıç KÖKTEN from the University of Ankara in 1946. Only a portion of the fifty-meter cave has been explored so far. The cave consists of three large inter-connected spaces where finds from the Palaeolithic, the Mesolithic, Neolithic, Chalcolithic, Bronze and later ages were discovered under 10.5 meters thick deposits. Apparently at one time the cave was used as a temple.

Displays in this corner contain examples of hand axes, scrapers made of flintstone, bone awls, burins as well as daggers and spear heads of horn. A skull of a Neanderthal child and a number of skulls and skeletons of Homo Sapiens are displayed along with the teeth and bones of extinct animals from the Palaeolithic Age. The head of a buffalo or of Elephanthus Meridionalis carved in stone is a fine example of a small artifact.

The show-cases of Palaeolithic Age are of special importance as they significantly reveal the thousands of years long of stone tool technology.

It is very objective that a primitive hand axe in the lower palaeolithic age turns out into a scraper or a dagger functionally by the age of upper palaeolithic.

Excavations in Karain cave the new term-have now been organized and directed by Prof. Işın YALÇINKAYA and her team of University of Ankara since 1988. These recent excavations lead both to the expansion of the site into international interest where scientists from all over the world would very well come and study and to the excavation itself to become one of the pinpoints in Turkey, as such must be revered as a miracle, that it endowed us with appreciable quantities of data to renew our knowledge of the physical world.

It is now suggested, depending on the latest data, that the first man-made stone tools found in Karain demonstrate a special technology - to be named "Karain stone technology"- dating back 200.000 years, and more, the suggestion that the time might go farther is to come forward.

This is high time we reminded that not alone for the world in Anatolia but for all

Mediterranean, that was the revolution of man-kind, thinking Neanderthal Men, besides the stone.

In the same cave are the messengers of the mankind to leap into age of agriculture, of the revolution of Neanderthal men an exceptional corner in the history; painted pottery samples, carbonized figs and wheat.

The cave has also a different significance by exhibiting the geological structure of the region as well as the flora and fauna of the early geological period apart from immensely and delicately rewarding us with the facts of the early art.

It enlightened that there happened a lake before the cave in Pleistosen and Holosen ages.

Finds from Bademağacı mound reveal the latest news from the region Neolithic age in the show-cases of first and second on the left of the hall. This mound has been excavated by Prof. Dr. Refik DURU and his team of the Istanbul University since 1993 and is located on, 2 km. North of Bademağacı village, the 50th km. from Antalya of the state road to Burdur. This is an oval shaped mound in 200 m. to 110 m. with height of 7 m.

By the data obtained so far, the first station backs in early Neolithic age and lasts all along until the termination of early Chalcolithic age (5.000/4.800 B.C.).

Not until the first bronze age (around 3.000 B.C.) had brought a new station which is probed to have lasted half of the age, had the mound suspended habitation for seemingly a long time after it was deserted.

The earliest station layer of the mound, early neolithic age, a 4-5 m. thick layer, has partially been excavated and is in a very good condition. Some of the dwelling units with their goods are now visible to the modern world almost intact. With al, in the spaces out of the units are the storages with clay swarmed plates.The station may now well be suggested to have been surrounded by walls for the purpose of defence. Among the found are variety of pottery and tools. The most common from of pottery with the tones of grey and brown, generally burnished, are the pottery with pot bellies, with finger or cylindiric handles, plates and dishes which have S profiles. Besides these a figurine head and tools made from stone and bone are also exhibited.

As the base has not still been reached, it is not known how many layers will be unearthed belonging to the neolithic age. Although a certain date remains unclear, it is suggested that the oldest early neolithic age station might be dated back to the second half of 7th cent.B.C. Remainings from the first bronze age have also been well preserved.

Stone basing of the stations in the form of at least four layers imply that the town, in that period, had significant importance and with rich fodder of pottery, the town, resembles, distinctively, the lines of pottery in the first bronze age like the ones in Elmalı-Semayük, in the South of West Anatolia. A flat idol, a stone made seal, golden earstuds, a bronze dagger are the artifacts from the period.

Excavation in Bademağacı inspire vast hope to help better understanding of prehistorical cultures in Antalya-Burdur region. These excavations will soon enlighten the period during which civilization converted from immigrant form of Palaeolithic and Mezolithic periods into the form of the agriculture based stationary life in Neolithic age.

Exhibited in the show case of Hacılar is a female fertility figurine and colorful- painted pottery unearthed at the Hacılar mound (in the province of Burdur), 150 km. North of Antalya, dates back to the Chalcolithic Period (5500-3000 B.C.).

The prehistoric site of Hacılar is about 1.5 km. from the modern village. Excavations by Prof. James MELLAART were made here between 1957 and 1960 under the auspices of the British Institute of Archaeology at Ankara. He uncovered nine building levels. Burials were discovered in eight of them. In the lowest, dating from the seventh millennium B.C., houses made of mud brick were found. During the Early Neolithic Period the people of the settlement were engaged in agriculture, pottery and did have domesticated dogs. The oldest know statuettes of the Anatolian Mother Goddess were found at Hacılar, dated to the sixth millennium B.C. with, staring eyes and massive legs. During the Chalcolithic period the settlement was surrounded by fortifications, the single room houses had plastered walls and ceilings, the inhabitants made pottery by hand and had learned to weave fabrics. Small, nude steatopygous type, reclining figures of the Mother Goddess found in this layer. Hacılar originally attracted attention with the colorful, painted pottery it yielded. The highly polished handmade vessels are most striking. They are representative of the Chalcolithic Period. The decoration of these vessels (red on buff) displays a special effect, making it difficult to determine which forms the background and which forms the design.

The Bronze Age finds on display in this hall come from a site called KarataŞ-Semayük near Elmalı, 120 km. North-West of Antalya. Karataş-Semayük is one of the major settlements of the Bronze Age (3000-1200 B.C.) in Anatolia.

The prehistorical site of Elmalı-Semayük and cemetery location called Karataş, were excavated under the direction of Prof. Machteld MELLINK from the University of Pennsylvania between 1963 and 1974 They have found nearly 500 tombs and a fortified house, which date from the Early Bronze Age (c. 3000-2000 B.C.). Most of the burials were in pithoi, large pottery jars, placed with their openings to the east. An examination of the skeletons has suggested that inhabitants of the site were well-built and well-nourished, but there was some evidence of arthritis and malaria and in a few cases of leprosy.

Earstuds, brush handles, bronze pins, and spearheads are some of the artifacts from Karataş-Semayük displayed at this section. At the end to the Hall of Natural History and Prehistory there is a reconstructed pitos burial from Karataş location, as well as several decorated pots and pithoi.

Gökhöyük findings are in the last show-case of the hall. The prehistoric site of Gökhöyük. excavated by the curators of the Antalya Museum in 1986, is located in, 29 km. North of Antalya city centre, Yeniköy region.

The mound is one of the rare elevations in Döşemealtı plain, 4 km. to Karain Cave, over travertine formation. The mound has been ruined to some extend but reveals that it is the first bronze age station such close to the sea. Unearthed pottery resembles in general lines, distinctively, the ones found in Elmalı-Semayük in the South of West Anatolia. Brush handles, bronze pins and spearheads are some of the artifacts of this section Gökhöyük displayed.

- Chipped Flint Stone tools
- Middle Palæolithic Period (Mousterian type)
- From Karain Cave

These Mousterian type tools are representative of Middle Palæolithic which is characterized by a developed flake tool industry. They comprise mainly side scrapers and triangular points. Other specimens include cores, blades, flakes, points, borers and knives.

- Stylzed Head of Horn
- Upper Palæolithic Period
- From Karain Cave

A stylized human head with narrow forehead, large nose and bearded face is carved on one end of a polished rib bone. It represents an artifact of unknown purpose created by Upper Palæolithic men.

21

- Two - Handled Painted Pot
- Baked clay from Hacılar,
  H: 42 cm.
- Early chalcolithic Period, second
  half of 6 th millennium B.C.
  Inv. No: 10.25.72

Round mouth with plain rim,
short cylindrical neck, carinated
ovoid body, flat base. Two vertical
lugs for suspension above carina-
tion. Buff paste, cream slip.
Decorated with geometric motifs on
the neck and body painted in red.
Hand-made.

- Baked clay Painted Bowl
- From Hacılar, H: 13.5 cm.
  D: 14.5 cm.
- Early chalcolithic Period, second
  half of 6 th millennium B.C.
  Inv.No: 13.25.72

Rounded mouth with slightly
flaring rim, slightly concave shallow
body, flat base. Buff paste, cream
slip. Decorations resembling stylized
double axes on the surface and on
the inside and stylized ram horns on
the tondo painted in red. Hand-
made.

- Baked clay Painted Bowl
- From Hacılar, H: 12.5 cm.
  D: 11 cm.
- Early Chalcolithic Period, second half of 6 th millennium B.C.
  Inv.No: A.1774

Round mouth with plain rim, slightly concave neck with spherical body, flat bottom. Two opposing protrusions on slightly carinated belly. Buff paste, cream slip. Decorated with horizontal bands painted in red. Hand-made.

- Baked clay Female Figurine
- From Hacılar, H: 9.9 cm.
- Early chalcolithic Period, second half of 6 th millennium B.C.
  Inv.No: 7.25.72

Standing figure of an obese nude woman. Head with slightly pronounced nose and ears resting on thick neck. Arms bent with hands resting on breasts. Wide shoulders and broad hips with pronounced navel and genitals. Buff paste. Hand-made.

23

Neolithic Pots and Figurine head
from Bademağacı mound. Late 6th.
- Early 5 th. millennium B.C.

- Baked clay Tankard
- From Elmalı-Semayük / Karataş, H: 16.9 cm. W:28 cm.
- Early Bronze Age, mid 3 rd millennium B.C. Inv.No: A.1347

Round mouth with flaring rim, concave neck, spherical body with slightly concave flattened base. Two loop handles round in section from below neck to base. Reddish-beige paste and slip. Burnished; hand-made.

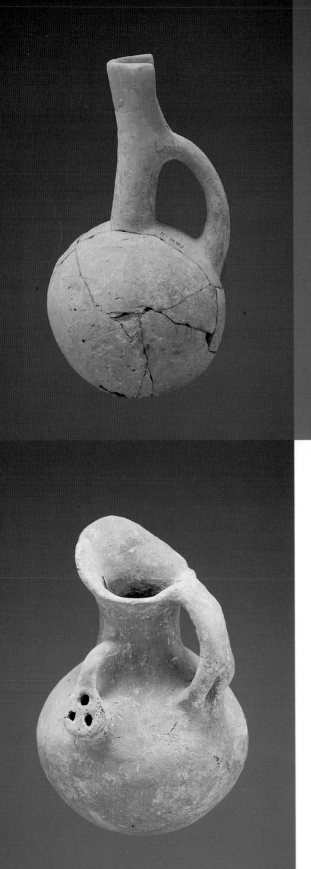

- Early Bronze Age Pots
- 2 nd half of 3rd millennium B.C
- From the Antalya Region.

- Pithos Burial-Baked clay and stone
- From Elmalı - Semayük / Karataş,
- Early Bronze Age, 3 rd millennium B.C.
- H:1.13m. Inv.No: A. 3709

Reflects traditional burial custom of Early Bronze Age men. A wide-bodied, hand-made pot, "Pithos", was placed on its side with the deceased laid in it in a contracted position called "hocker". Burial offerings which accompany the dead according to sex and age include jewelry, small beak-spouted pitchers or weapons. Mouth as well as body of the pithos then were covered with stones and earth.

- Marble Idol
- From Elmalı-Semayük / Karataş, H: 8.3 cm
- Early Bronze Age, 3 rd millennium B.C.
  Inv.No: A. 3338

Represents flattened and stylized forms of human anatomy: round head, long oblique neck, spade-shaped body. Carefully ground and profiled with abrasives.

- Small Pot
- Baked clay-Elmalı-Semayük
- Early Bronze Age.
- 1 st half of 3rd millennium B.C.

- Stamp Seal
- Baked clay-Elmalı-Semayük
- Early Bronze Age.
- Mid of 3rd millennium B.C.

- Spindle Whorl
- Baked clay-Elmalı-Semayük
- Early Bronze Age.
- 1 st half of 3rd millennium B.C.

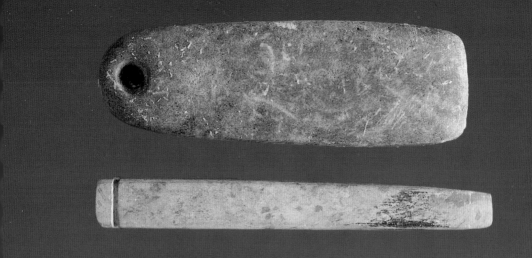

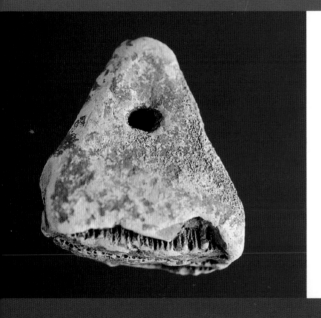

Pots-loom weights and brush handle from Gökhöyük, Early Bronze Age. 1st half of 3rd millennium B.C.

Joining Hall Number Two with Hall Number Three is a corridor where short inscriptions are displayed. Here are two stelae of particular importance one from Perge, the other from Aspendos. The former (fifth century B.C.) is in one of the oldest Pamphylian dialects of the region. It is a dedication to Artemis, the chief goddess of the city, under her local name "Wanessa Preiia."

Inscription of "Wanessa" is the only and the oldest evidence to enlighten not only the history of city of Perge but is also the document for the architecture in 5th cent. B.C. We do learn more about the monumental structures of the city thanks to this block.

The stele from Aspendos (third century B.C.) is important because it points to the existence of a temple of Artemis in Aspendos. It also indicates that during the period of domination by the Ptolemies, Aspendos enjoyed a remarkable degree of independence. "When Apollonios, son of Democharis, was the governor (demiourgos) and a full meeting of the assembly (ecclesia), the people of Aspendos made the following decision. Since the city has been honored by Pamphylians, Lycians, Cretans, Greeks and Pisidians who are with Democles and Leonidas and since, like King Ptolemaios they are worthy people and of benefit to our city, they and their children shall receive the title of citizen and benefactor, a stele shall be placed in the temple of Artemis bearing their names of their fathers; if any one of them should so desire, they can be registered with a tribe (phyla). The cost of this will be paid by the city. This was agreed. Menandros, son of Elisotos of Aspendos. Petrakis. son of Sophanes of Miletos"

The inscripted epitaph and a mile stone, brought from one of those Roman roads in the North of Antalya which belongs to Septimius Severus period are the final traces in the hall.

Limestone Honorary Inscription from Aspendos. This inscription is very important because it shows not only that there was a temple of Artemis at Aspendos, but also that even when the city belonged to the kingdom of the Ptolemies it was able to make independent decisions such as this democratic and generous one bestowing citizenship on the foreigners residing there. 3rd century B.C. Antalya Museum. Inv.No: A. 165

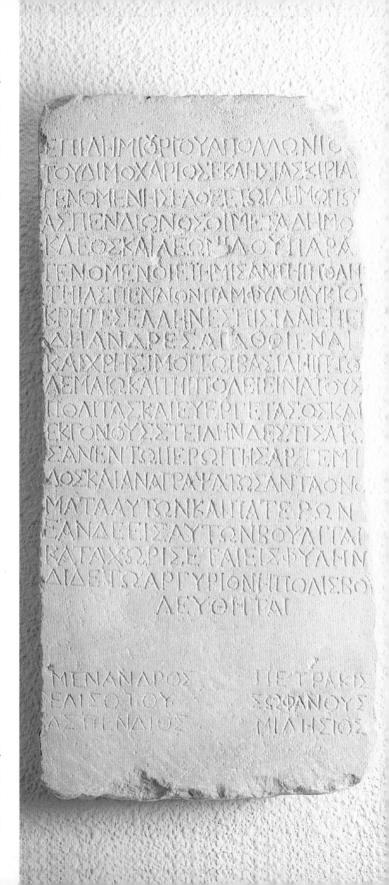

Limestone Dedicatory Inscription from Perge. 5th century B.C. L: 0.91 m. W: 0.37 m. Rectangular block bearing an inscription in Pamphylian dialect: "Klemutas, son of L'Faramus of Wasir Fotas tribe has dedicated this monument to Pergaean Goddess Wanessa Preiia in accordance with an order conveyed to him during his sleep".

HALL OF RESCUE EXCAVATIONS (Hall III)

Hall number 3 or literally "Hall of Rescue Excavations" holds the content of two recent rescue excavations by the curators of the Antalya Museum.

Village of Karaçallı, 7 km. South of Aksu where is at the 16th km of Alanya - Antalya state road is the site for the first excavation.

The excavations, reputed as "Karaçallı Necropolis Excavations", have started in 1991. This burial ground, dating back to 5th cent.BC., located between ancient cities of Perge and Magydus, has an extreme importance to the archaeology of the region as it samples the pottery of pure classical period (5th-4th cent.BC.).

By the entrance of the hall is the exhibited Red-figured Column Crater, the most significant of finds. The "Tibet Krater", named so to honour the curator who first unearthed it, hosts two methops on the body one of which is decorated with four, while other with three figures. Regarding the figures as well as the forming, "Tibet Krater" bears a striking resemblance to those Sicilian artists' vases who painted pots similar to the Attician artists'.

Along with this magnificent sample, pottery samples, again red figured and dating to 4th cent.BC., are also exhibited in the first two show-cases of the hall.

Other show-cases in the hall silently host the magnificent beauty of the Phrygian artifacts thanks to the second rescue excavation. These all have been uncovered in 1986-87 in tumuli around "Çağıltemeller", near the village of Bayındır in Elmalı Plain. Each of these late 8th or early 7th cent.BC. constructions was of a group of small mounds hidden beneath piles of rubble. Not alone are these artifacts from the tumuli the most suggestive finds but they also are the finds to cause happen a new dimension to the Anatolian history. These pure Phrygian artifacts, like the similar ones from tomb of King Midas of Gordion, have drawn new question to Phrygian history and geography which have still been discussed among archaeologists of the modern world.

Among the finds of tumulus C excavated in 1986 and concluded to be a cremation, are two bronze protomes (decorative bronze griffin heads), and on the edge of the rims of the badly damaged cauldrons; a bronze ceremonial symbol being of a ring with there bunches of phallic knobs, the bronze ompholos bowls, fibulae, a dagger, a spearhead and arrowheads of iron. Gold earrings, lion head and duck shaped pins are also among the most impressive finds coming up into daylight from the darkness of the deep cremation. The earrings are given a prior importance as they were the igniting goods to set up boldly onto the excavations indicating the rich fodder of tumuli.

Among the finds from inhumation tumulus D, excavated in 1987, small sheet silver cauldrons with ring handles, bull heads fastened to t-shaped attachments, a silver ladle with inscriptions in Phrygian and a small cauldron deserve special interest.

The same tumulus also have gifted to modern world two pure silver belts one of which had kept its originality in excellent condition while with the other identical one, both appear in incised geometric designing with probability of having been lined with leather, cloth or felt.

A number of silver bowls with raised boss (ompholos) wrapped in cloth have also been unearthed in the tumulus D. These bowls were either plain or decorated with radiating floral designs on the outside, clearly representing the well known Phrygian variants. The majority of the fibulae placed in a grave were for the dead in the tumuli.

The practice of ornamenting with silver plaques is most Phrygian. The embossed silver appliques and ivory plaques had possibly been used as decoration to coffins, furniture or harnesses. Sheet silver breast plates for horses and iron bits from the same burial zone are well representing the Anatolian horsemanship in the Iron Age. In tumulus D the archaeologists found an exquisite ivory statue of a standing female figure with two children. They also covered a silver figurine of a priestess. Wearing a tail headdress, severe in mien, she stands with folded hands. Now these are on exhibition in central show-case.

The present exhibition of Phrygian artifacts at the Antalya Museum is a rich colletion of the splendid and unusual cultural heritage of the Phrygians who lived in the North of Antalya.

In front of the Hall of the Phrygians there are two bell kraters and column krater. The column krater from the necropolis of Aspendos dates back to the fifth century B.C. It show three youths in a merry celebration, dancing vigorously while holding drinking cups. On the reverse side there are three youths depicted arming themselves. The bell krater with red figures is decorated on one side with Dionysos seated among the meanads and a dancing satyr. On the reverse, another satyr is shown between two maenads.

- Red Figured Column Krater (Tibet Krater)
- Found in 1991, from the Classical Necropolis of Karaçallı
- H: 43.6 cm. Inv.No: 1.12.91
- Classical Period, end of 5th or begining of 4th century B.C.

Red-figured column-krater decorated two metops on the body. One of which is decorated with four, while other with three youths having fun and drinking. Each picture field bordered above by a kymation.

- Red Figured Bell Krater
- Found in 1991, from the Classical Necropolis of Karaçallı
- H: 23.8 cm. Inv.No: 2.12.91
- Classical Period, end of 5th or begining of 4th century B.C.

Red-figured bell-krater showing seated Pan who play flute and armed Athena in front of him.

- Golden Earrings
- Found in 1986, from the cremation of Tumulus C at Elmalı-Bayındır
- L: 2.5-3.5 cm.- D: 0.9 cm. - Wt: 1.95.2 gr. Inv.No: 5.16.86 - 6.16.86
- Phrygian Period, late 8th or early 7th centuries B.C.

   Each earring composed of a hollow double cone bead with four strands of woven gold wire, each terminating in a gold bead. Two beads missing.

- Electrum Pin Head in Shape of a duck
- Found in 1986, from the cremation of Tumulus C at Elmalı - Bayındır
- H: 1.7 cm.- W: 2.35 cm. Wt: 3.48 gr. Inv.No: 4.16.86
- Phrygian Period, late 8th or early 7th centuries B.C.

Pin head in shape of a squatted duck made of sheet electrum. Shaft is missing. Eyes and beak indicated by incision, feat- hers on the body by granulation. Hollow-cast.

- Electrum Pin Head in Shape of a Lion
- Found in 1986, from the cremation of Tumulus C at Elmalı - Bayındır
- H: 1.8 cm.- W: 1.1 cm. Wt: 2.13 gr. Inv.No: 3.16.86
- Phrygian Period, late 8th or early 7th centuries B.C.

Pin head in shape of a fierce looking snarling lion's head with open jaws and protruding tongue, made of sheet electrum. Shaft is missing. Mane, muzzle, forehead, contours of the eyes decorated in granulation. Hollow-cast.

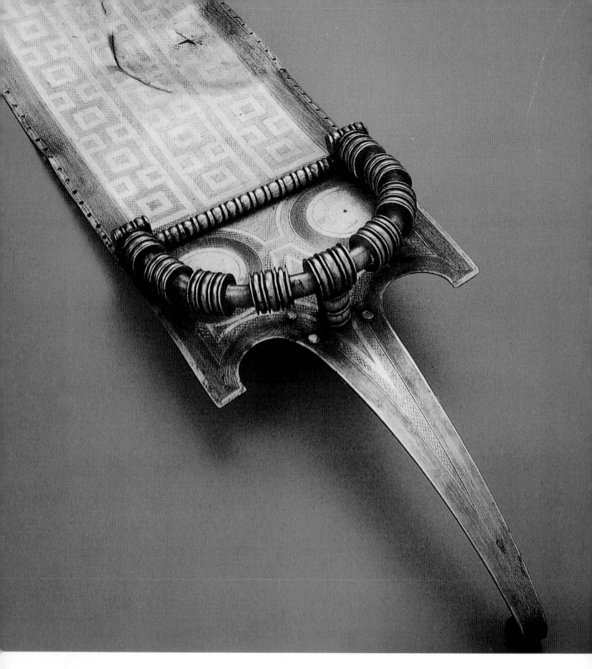

- Silver Belt
- Found in 1987, from the Tumulus D at Elmalı-Bayındır
- L: 143 cm.-W: 9.2 cm. - Wt: 740 gr. Inv.No: 15.16.86 - 6.16.86
- Phrygian Period, late 8th or early 7th centuries B.C.

Formed of a continuous strip of sheet silver with a long hook at one end. A fibula-like attachment decorated with milled bead-and-reel mouldings is hinged on to the belt, making a sort of handle which would have helped in taking the hook in one of ten notches on a long curved tongue at the other end of the belt. Decorated in openwork; the tongue with rounded end is hinged on to the belt proper by means of a moulded attachment. Belt strip decorated with incised, linked squares in three parallel rows with incised small squares used as filling ornaments.

- Silver Statuette of A Priestess
- Found in 1987, from the Tumulus D at Elmalı-Bayındır
- H: 12.4 cm.-W: 3 cm. - Wt: 48 gr. Inv.No: 11.21.87
- Phrygian Period, late 8th or early 7th centuries B.C.

A frontal standing figure of a priestess draped in a long, belted, fine pleated elbow-length robe of columnar shape reaching to the ground. A tall headdress crowns the head and is divided into three horizontal registers by parallel bands; two registers filled with incised dotted diamond pattern, central one with dotted zigzags. Face with severe expression is framed by thick coils of hair on each temple; at the back of the head hair is shaved off. Arms bent at the elbow, hands clasped at the front. Plain bracelets encircle each wrist and a necklace of large beads arranged like a bead-and-reel moulding decorates the neck. Hollow-cast, details incised.

- Ivory Statuette of a Goddess
- Found in 1987, from the Tumulus D at Elmalı-Bayındır
- H: 17 cm.-W: 5.4 cm.
  Inv.No: 2.21.87
- Phrygian Period, late 8th or early 7th centuries B.C.

A frontal standing female figure holding a child with her right hand and grasping a nude child by his left leg who straddles her left shoulder. The group has been carved from a single block with the solid oblong base on which it stands.

The female figure wears a foldless long robe with long-sleeves and a veil. Both edges of the veil are gathered at the front of the lower body and tucked into figure's belt. Hem of the garment is slightly raised to show the toes. A high headdress of nearly cylindrical form crowns the head and holds a long veil beneath which frames the straight short hair surrounding the face.

The standing child is also clad in a similar, but richly patterned garment decorated with double hooks and hooked swastikas within bands. Hairdress composed of columnar locks hanging at the back and incised in a herring-bone pattern; snail-like locks on each temple. Faces of the famale figure and the standing child bear an archaic smile; head of the straddling child missing. A rectangular tenon hole on the apex of the headdress of the female figure.

- Silver Petaled Omphalos Bowl
- Found in 1987, from the Tumulus D at Elmalı-Bayındır
- H: 4.2 cm.- D. (mouth) :15.7 cm. Wt: 360 gr. Inv.No: 7.21.87
- Phrygian Period, late 8th or early 7th centuries B.C.

Hemispherical bowl with thickened rim. Omphalos decorated with an incised rosette in the center; petals in high relief on the body. Raised from one piece of silver plaque.

- Silver Cauldron with socket Attachments
- Found in 1987, from the Tumulus D at Elmalı-Bayındır
- H: 13.6 cm.-D: 14.3 cm. Wt: 845 gr. Inv.No: 11.21.87
- Phrygian Period, late 8th or early 7th centuries B.C.

Small cauldron with flattened offset rim and spherical body. Two opposing vertical sockets for ring handles cast together with T-shaped plaques are attached to the vessel below the rim. Ring handles missing. Incised inscription below the rim outside. Raised from one piece of silver plaque.

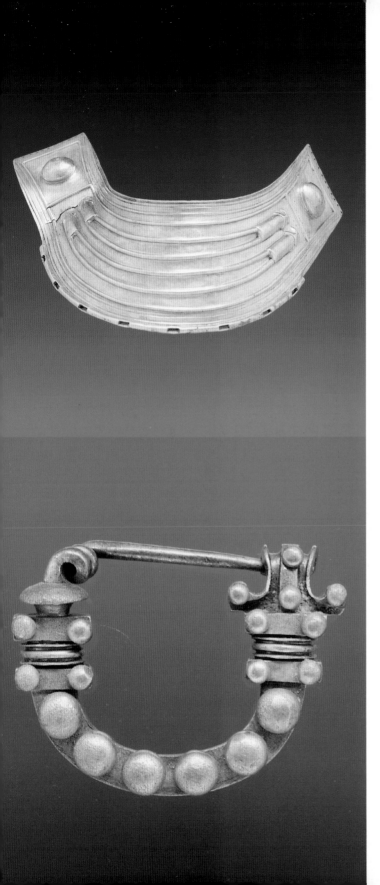

- Silver Horse's Breastplate
- Found in 1987, from the
  Tumulus D at Elmalı-Bayındır
- W: 9.2 cm.- Wt: 402 gr.
  Inv.No: 62.21.87
- Phrygian Period, late 8th or early
  7th centuries B.C.

Crescent-shaped plaque made of sheet silver and bordered with parallel ridges along the edges. A row of stitch-holes along the straight ends and small rectangular perforations along the convex edge, probably designed for tassels. Between two metopes with central bosses, four parallel ridges in groups of two, each group terminating in spool-or hoof-shaped finials at both ends.Decoration in repoussé.

- Silver Fibula
- Found in 1987, from the
  Tumulus D at Elmalı-Bayındır
- W: 3.2 cm. - Th: 06 cm.
  Wt: 15 gr. Inv.No: 26.21.87
- Phrygian Period, late 8th or early
  7th centuries B.C.

Arched fibula with bow rectangular in section, decorated with round-headed studs of various sizes. Cast made.

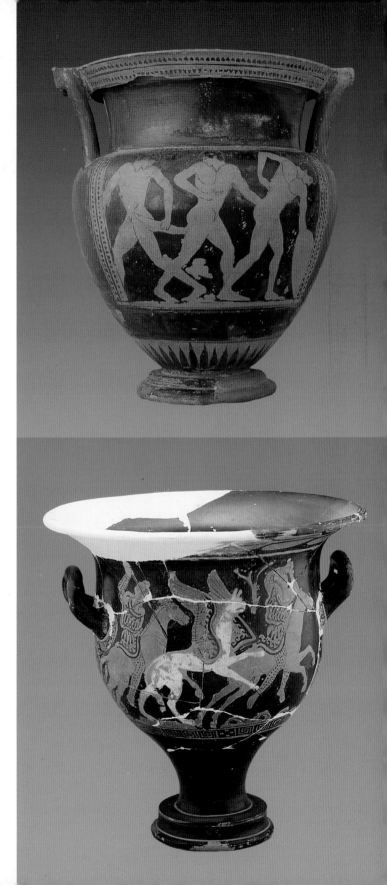

- Red Figured Column Krater
- Found from the Classical Necropolis of Aspendos
- H: 36 cm. Inv.No: A.377
- Classical Period, end of 5th or begining of 4th century B.C.

Red-figured column-krater decorated with three youths having fun and drinking on one face, and another group of three youths arming on the other. Each picture field bordered above by a kymation. Rays on top of the rim and above the base. Wheel-made.

Gold necklace from the Elmalı-Bayındır village dating from the 4th century B.C. and offering a wide variety of decoretive elements: Suspended a corns and beads. Inv.No: 4-25.26.89

- Red Figured Calyx Krater
- Found from Varsak of Antalya
- H: 43 cm. Inv.No: A.505
- Classical Period, 5th century B.C.

Red -Figured calyx -krater decorated with Dionysos seated among Mæanads and a dancing Satyr on one face, another Satyr between two Mæanads on the other. Picture field bordered below by a continuous band of mæanders to the left, interrupted every four mæanders by a cheeker-board square and zigzags filled with rosettes. Wheel-made.

THE GALLERY OF THE GODS (Hall IV)

The Antalya Museum possesses priceless statues recovered from the ancient city of Perge excavated by Prof. Dr. A.Müfit MANSEL and Prof.Dr.Jale İNAN since 1946. The Museum's collection of statues is a unique exhibit of the Pergaean school of sculpture that occupied a special place during the period of Roman sovereignity in Asia Minor. We know that in capital cities of the Roman provinces, the official and public areas such as Porticos, Nymphaeurns, Baths and Agoras, were decorated with statues. Many excavations in Antalya prove that the Romans favored the baths as the place to decorate with the statues. This was also true in recent excavations in the South Bath of Perge.

Among these is the section _ - VII with a particular importance due to the plinths of the statues indicating the same inscription on them.

Prof. Jale İNAN suggests the section and the statues as: "Section VII in the South Bath of Perge flies open into Frigidarium with an enormous archway. On the North-South axis of the bath there lies this section by 46.80 m. to 13.40 m. This is the location to constitute, by columns, a gallery onto the West and North porticoes of Palaestra on the longer east side. By the excavation of the gallery, artifacts; heads, torsos, complete pieces and major fragments found in the section make up 38 samples of statues. Of all the traces, 11 had been vowed by a man named Klaudius Peison, as resulted from the inscriptions on the plinths. That is why we did name the gallery as "Gallery of Klaudius Peison".

This is to say that the statues exhibited in the museum separately but with Klaudius Peison inscription are all from the same section.

Another favored place to display the statues was in the center of the city. More than one hundred statues are grouped and displayed according to their characteristics and types, in various halls and galleries.These statues are now in the "Gallery of the Gods" and the "Gallery of the Emperors" of the Antalya Museum.Of the 50 statues included in this two galleries, 20 come from the South Bath of Perge, 27 come from other parts of the city of province.

When you compare the Roman Statues in the Antalya Museum to those in other museums around the world, you will find that the Museum in Antalya has one of the most enriching and quality collections. Almost all the statues belong to the second century A.D., the Golden Age of the Roman Empire. The rich discoveries in Pamphylia, at Antalya and surrounding areas show that the region was prolific in producing marble sculpture of the highest quality in this bright period. "Every true work is rooted in tradition, but is also imprinted with it's own distinctiveness. For this reason it must not only be put in its place in history, but also recognized as a unique place of art."

This is always true of the idealized Roman sculpture. The Roman artist used Greek sculpture as a model and created his work of art like the original, according to his own talent and personality. Or he may have created portrait statues of persons in his time period and given them the characterists of Greek models. From these statues one can determine the exact artist or his school and studio. This is apparent from the different copies of the same period but discovered in different locations. These differences are apparent in statues from the cities of Side and Perge, which are generally typical of art in this province.

Many of the statues found in excavations at Perge show that Perge had a distinctive style of sculpture compared to other cities of the province. Such style consists of a strict and definite outline, especially portrait statues. The different shapes are clearly outlined, transitions into details are sudden. One can see this especially at the transition from hair to skin and from chin to neck. Wrinkles on forehead were made with clear strokes.The portraits of the Emperors and their families do not follow the official portraits, but have their own unique style. This is evidence of a unique sculpture tradition, at least for the second century A.D. in Perge.

Hall number 4 contains some of the major treasures of the museum. In the Gallery of the Gods the statues on display date back to second century A.D., Perge. They include an excellent statue of Hermes tying his sandals as well as statues of the Egyptian trinity of Serapis, Isis, and Harpocrates. A statue of Artemis with a part of the face and one leg missing, a statue of Athena in good condition and statues of Apollo, Hygeia, Tyche, Aphrodite, Artemis, Nemesis and a statue of a pensive Dioscuros are some of the major works in the Hall of Gods which is appropriately dominated by a fine statue of Zeus.

A finely porous white marble from Proconnesos (present-day Marmara Island) has been used for all of these sculptures.

Zeus, the king of gods, the father of gods and man, is depicted standing in all grandeur. In his hands he held a globe symbolizing his sovereignty and a thunderbolt, both of which are missing today. His sacred animal, the eagle is by his right leg.

Aphrodite, the goddess of beauty is shown in the nude, standing. The particular statue of Aphrodite is a copy of the original known as the Capua Aphrodite carved by the famous sculptor Scopas in the fourth century B.C. The Pergaean sculptor has taken the liberty of adding a shield in Aphrodite's hands. On the shield is inscribed the name of Klaudios Peison, the Pergaean patron of arts.

The goddess of fortune, Tyche (Fortuna) is also the protector of cities. On the head of the statue of Tyche, is a crown depicting the Pergaean city walls-symbolizing her patronage of the city.

On the shoulders of the statue of Hygieia, the daughter of the god of health, Asclepios. There are two snakes, which as the caduceus is still the symbols of medicine and pharmacy.

Apollo, the god of music and fine arts, is depicted nude, as an idealized male figure.

With her shield, armor, and helmet, the statue of Athena, the goddess of war and handicrafts, prossesses the characteristics of an original sculpture of the Athena Parthenos type that dates back to the fourth century B.C.

One of the twins, the Dioscuri (Castor and Pollux), offspring of the god Zeus from Leda, stands to the left of Zeus. With his Phrygian helmet, he represents a youth with his sword on his back.

In the same hall, another Pergaean statue of Aphrodite made after Praxiteles' Aphrodite of the fourth century B.C., is shown as a totally nude youth.

Artemis, the main goddess of Perge, however, is depicted as a proud, robed young woman. In her hands she is supposed to carry a bow and an arrow, both of which are missing today. On her back is a quiver.

Nemesis, the goddess of retributive justice who punished grudge and pride, is portrayed as a proud and attractive young woman. She carries symbols of measurement to measure behavior, but they are missing from this particular statue. Next to her left foot there is a griffon, her symbol.

The statue "Hermes Tying His Sandals" located in the center of the hall is a masterpiece of Pergaean sculpture. The messenger god is portrayed in a momentary pose, recalling the famous fourth century B.C. sclupture made by Lysippos in the same form. This particular statue is even more noteworthy for making possible the identification of the other copies presently housed in various European museums.

At the entrance of the Gallery of the Gods are there four statues three of which depict gods of Egyptian origin. Osiris, the chief god of Egyptian mythology, is shown seated next to his wife, Isis. Their son Horus (Harpocrates) is portrayed as a nude youth standing.

The statue placed last in the same hall belongs to Artemis who is shown running. The swiftness of her motion drapes her clothes. She must have carried a bow and an arrow both of which are missing today. There is a quiver on her back. The style of the statue is reminiscent of the sculptor Leohares' Artemis of Versailles, dated the fourth century B.C.

- Statue of Zeus (Jupiter)
- Found in Perge 1970, at the Northern Nymphaeum
- Fine-grained white marble H. 2.22 m. (7 ft. 3 in.)
- Roman, second cent. A.D. Inv.No: A . 3729

The statue of the greatest of all Olympians was found from the nymphaeum in Perge, at the North end of the main street. Zeus was decorating one of the niches of the monumental fountain. Six large and six small pieces were broken off that fit together perfectly. Missing are the scepter held in his left hand a finger from his right hand and the globe. His weight carried on his right leg, the left leg being set somewhat back-wards and to one side. He is dressed in a himation over his left shoulder, which extends over his right hip and drops down to his ankle and wears sandals on his feet.

Thick wavy hair and beard frame the face of this god portrayed as a strong adult man. His head is turned slightiy to the right. His hair is held with a band around his head. His symbol, the eagle is in front of a support beam next to his right leg. This statue is typical of the classical period (5th cent B.C.) but was made by sculptors Pergeian in the second century A.D.

Apollon
Perge İ.S.2.yy.
2nd Cent.A.D.

- Statue of Apollo
- Found in Perge l971, at the Northern Nymphaeum
- Fine-grained white marble H. 2.10 m. (6 ft.10 in.)
- Roman, second cent. A.D. Inv.No: 3866

The statue of Apollo was discovered in 1971 during excavation of the Monumental Nymphaeum at the Northern end of the main street of Perge. Apparently it decorated a niche of the Nymphaeum, where 13 fragments were found at the Western wing of the building. The fragments were fitted together at each break. In the reconstruction of the statue missing pieces were filled with Gypsum. He is pictured in this Roman copy of the second century A.D. as a tall naked young man. The weight of the body is supported on the right leg and on this side the contour of the hip forms a strongly protruding curve. The left leg is bent at the knee and extended to the side. His posture facial expression and hairdo remind one of the statues of the Hellenistic period.

- Statue of Athena (Minerva)
- Found in Perge 1982, in the pool of section İ-8 at the South-Bath
- Fine-grained white marble
  H.1.84 m. (6 ft.)
  Roman, second cent. A.D.
- (Antonine period)
  Inv.No: 1.22.82

The statue of Athena was found in 1982, during excavations of the South Bath of Perge from pool of section İ-8. The statue is intact except for her missing hands and shield. It was placed on a pillar of the West wall of the room as part of a pillar. The goddess is represented in this statue as a young woman wearing a himation over her chiton. The weight of the body is supported on the left leg. The right leg is bent at the knee and extended to the side-and back. The armor over her chest is decorated with a fish scale pattern. Over her breasts is a head of Medusa. She wears thick leather sandals. On her head is a Corinthian helmet. Her face is framed by hair parted in the middle. She is looking upward with a sad but benevolent and determined facial expression. The pedestal on the base at her left probably supported a shield held by the goddess. The original statue of this type goes back to the fourth century B.C. This Roman copy belongs to the last half of the second century A.D. (Antonine period).

- Statue of Nemesis
- Found in Perge 1968, in the court of the Late Roman Gate-Way
- Fine-grained white marble H. 1.85 m. (6 ft. 1 in.)
- Roman, second cent. A.D. Inv.No: A . 3373

This statue of Nemesis was discovered at Perge in 1968 during excavation of the court of the Late Roman Gate-Way. It was broken into 14 fragments.

Both of her arms are broken near the elbow. Nemesis is represented in this statue as a tall young woman standing beside a griffon. The weight of the body rests on the left leg and the contour of the hip at this side forms a wide curve. The right leg is relaxed and drawn slightly backwards. She is wearing a peplos made of thin material so that the forms of the body are outlined beneath. The peplos has slipped down from the left shoulder leaving the breast exposed on this side and this producing a folded roll that cuts diagonally across the body. Like a number of other resembling it, the original belongs to the Hellenistic period (2nd cent.B.C.).

- Statue of Hermes Tying His Sandal (Sandal-binder of Lysippos)
- Found in Perge 1977, in the Palaestra of the South-Bath
- Fine-grained white marble H. 1.62 m. (5 ft. 4 in)
- Roman, second cent. A.D. Inv.No: 3.25.77

The statue of Hermes tying his sandal has rightly become one of the most remarkable statues of the museum. It is a masterpiece of sculpture and is of great scientific and artistic importance. This is in the best condition and most complete copy discovered to date.

The original is ascribed to the great sculptor Lysippos of the Hellenistic period in the second half of the fourth century B.C. Other coples in Copenhagen, Paris, Munich and the Vatican have caused discussions for the last 200 years regarding the missing parts and effect of faulty restorations. For this reason, Hermes of Perge, a masterpiece free of restorations, is from a scientific point of view, very important. It will contribute answers to questions that have been a problem for 200 years. Hermes of Perge will find his place in the literature of archaeology as the best example of his type.

- Statue of Artemis (Diana)
- Found in Perge 1968, at the Late Roman Gate-Way
- Fine-grained white marble
  H. 1.78 m. (5 ft. 10 in.)
- Roman, second cent. A.D.
  Inv.No: A . 3308

The statue of Artemis was discovered during an excavation in 1968 at the Roman Gate of Perge. Apparently it stood in front of the gate. It has been reconstructed from 8 fragments which fit together neatly at each break. Except for the bow in her left hand and the arrow in her right hand the statue is in good condition. The weight of the body rests on the right leg while the left leg is slightly bent at the knee and extended forwards and laterally. She is dressed in a peplos which is tied below the chest and extends down to her toes. She carries a silver quiver on her back as a symbol for hunting. The statue's posture, its clothing as well as facial features make this Roman copy of a second century A.D. statue a good representative of Classical period (5 th cent. B.C.) statues.

- Marble Head of Apollo
- Found from Perge 1978
- Fine-graind white marble, H:35 cm.
- Roman ,second century A.D. Inv.No: 1.11.78

Neck broken around the base. Head crowned by a laurel wreath. Wavy hair parted in the middle, falling down the nape. Eyelids indicated by lines, eyebrows, pupils and irises clearly pronounced. Eyes gazing into distance.

THE HALL OF SMALL OBJECTS (Hall V)

Hall Number 5 is devoted to small works of art found in the different locations of the region and wares recovered from the Mediterranean. On the right-hand wall before the first show-case shown statuette of Aphrodite which was found in Arykanda in 1990. Arykanda has been excavated since 1971, under the direction of Prof. Cevdet BAY-BURTLUOĞLU from Ankara University.

The city, located on the slopes of Village of Arif on the mid point of where is today Elmalı - Finike state road, is one of those mountainous Lycian cities with the right of one only vote in the union. By the excavation next to the bouleuterion, the unearthed piece is the statuette of Aphrodite in Kyrene type. Hair in the piece is down to the neck in two folds. Left hand holds the himation, covering the lower half of the body. Eros sits on the dolphin on the left.

The first show-case contains some figurines and vases from the Mycenaean Period (the 12th century B.C.). There is a remarkable terra-cotta vase head believed to come from Cyprus (the sixth century B.C.). The second case contains some vases from the Classical Period (the fifth century B. C.) and a collection of Classical and Hellenistic small vases or lecythoi, (the fifth century to third century B. C.). The third case displays some Hellenistic figurines and vases (the thrid and second century B. C.). The moulded relief of a decorative ceramic wine server, the oinochoe, is the most impressive piece in the case. A female figurine in high relief stands in front of an altar. Cladin a chiton and himation, she holds a glass container, the phiale, in her right hand; she carries the horn of plenty over her left arm. From an inscription incised around her shoulder she is identified as the Egyptian Queen Berenice II, the wife of Ptolemy III. The decoration is moldcast with light blue glaze.

The second century bronze statuette of a nude Apollo (recoverd from Seleuceia), the bearded Priapos shown carrying fruit inside his skirt which is pulled up and supported by his erect phallus (unearthed at Aspendos), the bronz head of Attis wearing a Phrygian helmet (discovered in Perge), and bronze statuette of Hercules with a club (unearthed in Fogla) are especially noteworthy, which exhibited in seperate show-cases at the center of the hall.

On the second wall both in two show-cases there contain some finds from Patara excavation. Patara, the leading sea port of Lycia, has been excavated since 1988 by the coordination and under supervise of Prof. Fahri IŞIK of Mediterranean University of Antalya.

According to Prof. IŞIK;

"Name Patara is mentioned for first time as "Patar" in a hieroglyph inscription of the Hittite King Tuthalia IV. dated 13 th century B.C., the Lycian name is "Pttara". The city had never lost her importance as one of the two most important oracl center of

Apollo with Delos, being the main harbour of the area. Patara was one of the six Lycian cities with the posession of three votes in the Lycian league and she was the leader of this league in the Hellenistic time: "caput gentis". The Lycian - Pamphylian province of Rome was ruled by the governor general in Patara. She was a metropolis during the Byzantian Period. The city also acquired a high honor among the Christian circles as the birthplace of St. Nicholaos. The city has also historical date-palms, characteristic to North Africa.

Patara is also important with her special type of tombs. These had been chosen due to the naturel structure of the area. This early Anatolian type of tombs has been discovered in - situ for the first time in Lycia. Now the tradition of the tomb architecture and burial customs of Lycia are to be rewritten by those new evidences.

There must be many others like these on the hills of Patara. They have one chamber, which are entered by a dromos covering a big slab stone. Numerous skeletons, found in - situ, clearly show the continuously use of them as family tombs. Each tomb includes 4-8 bodies, with their private goods, tomb goods and gifts, like terra-cotta statuettes, unguentariums, bronze mirrors, and golden jewelry. One of the most interesting findings is a bronze ink pot with black ink in. The kind and quality of the objects are parallel with the professions and economic positions of their owners. For instance the skeleton near the inkpot must have belonged to a scribe. And the objects together with the skeletons give information about the sex and the age of their owners. The graves are dated by the archaeological material, especially with coins, to the late Hellenistic and early Roman period. (2nd cent.B.C. - 1st cent.A.D.)"

On the third wall of this hall there is a display of amphorae, stone and metal anchors, objects, and pottery recovered from the Mediterranean. These date from the third century to the fourteenth century A.D.

On the last edge of this hall there are four show-cases which contains metal, terra-cotta, marble and glass finds from the different sites. First show-case contains some bronze vases, figurines, weights, and a decorated silver dish from the Roman Period (second and fourth centuries A.D.). The silver dish from Side shows the head of Athena in high relief. She wears a crested Corinthian helmet and carries a spear and shield. She has an aegis with the head of Medusa on her chest. Her hair falls loosely over her neck. The second case contains some metal and terra-cotta lamps from the Roman Period.The third case contains some heads of figurines made of marble and last case contains some glass made objects from the 3rd cent.B.C. to the 6th cent.A.D.

Leaving Hall Number 5, near the entrance to Hall Number 6 there is a fine statue of Marsyas and the headless statue of Apollo with a lyre competing in a musical contest. And beside of them "seated Mousa" for voting of the competition.

- Baked clay Mykenaean Pot
- H:14 cm. Inv.No:2957
- 13th - 12th century B.C.
- Mykenaean Period

- Baked clay Jug with trefoil mounth
- H:35 cm. Inv.No:28.21.72
- 5th century B.C.
- Classical Period

- Baked clay Squat Lekythos
- Found from Xanthos in 1950, H:10.4 cm.
- Classical Period, 5th century B.C. Inv.No: A.458

Red figure Lekythos decorated with a female head facing to the right on black burnished ground; a tendril or scroll ornament to her right. Whell-made.

- Oinochoe with Moulded Relief Decoration
- From the Lycian Akropolis of Xanthos
- Baked clay- H: 24.6 cm.
- Hellenistic Period, 3rd century B.C. Inv.No: A.514

Oinochoe with a trefoil mouth and ring base. Decorated with a female figure in high relief in front of an altar, facing to the left. Clad in a chiton and himation, she is holding a phiale in her right and is carrying a fertility horn over her left arm. Identified as the Egyptian queen Berenice II, the wife of Ptolemy III, on the basis of an inscription incised around the shoulder. Decoration mould-cast; light blue glazed. Wheel-made.

- Gold Diadem and perfume flasks from the Hellenistic period tomb of Patara. 1st century B.C.

- Bronze Head of Attis
- Found from Perge in 1971, H: 11 cm. H:0.22 m.
- Roman Period, 2nd century A.D. Inv.No: A.3877

   Head of Attis, the Phrygian deity, wearing a typical Phrygian cap with a decorated tip covering the delicate curls of hair. Round, slightly swollen face with pronounced pupils and parted lips. Broken around the neck. Hollow-cast.

- Marble Statuette of Priapos
- Found from the Alacami village of Serik . H: 45 cm.
- Roman period, 2nd cuntury A.D. Inv.No: A. 1015

   Standing figure of Priapos wearing a low cylindrical headdress and draped in a longsleeved cloak reaching to the ground at the back. He is shown carrying fruits inside of his skirt which is pulled up and supported by his erect phallus.

- Bronze Statuette of Apollon
- Found in Seleuceia (Şıhlar)/Manavgat, H: 53 cm.
- Roman Period, 2nd century A.D. Inv.No: A.615

Standing figure of nude Apollon with his left arm raised.Wavy hair strands frame the oval face and are tied in a knot above the forehead, with tresses of hair falling over both shoulders behind the neck. Slightly open mouth, straight nose, pupils of the eyes indicated. Right arm and leg from the knee down and left leg missing. Hollow-cast.

- Bronze Statuette of Herakles
- Found from Pogla (Çomaklı), H:43 m.
- Roman Period, 2nd century A.D. Inv.No: 1.26.77

Standing figure of a naked Herakles (Hercules), his head turned to the right, on a rectangular base with feet in shape of lion's paws surmounted by a round pedestal. The weary hero's weight on the left leg; the right leg with bent knee set to the side and back. He is resting on his club placed on a bull's head. Lower left arm missing. Cast.

- Marble Statuette of Aphrodite
- Found in Arykanda (Arif) in 1990, H: 78 cm.
- Roman Period, 2nd century A.D. Inv.No: 14.33.90

Standing figure of Aphrodite in Kyrene type. Hair in the piece is down to the neck in two folds. Left hand holds the himation, covering the lower half of the body. Eros sits on the dolphin on the left.

- Decorated Silver Dish
- Found in Gazipaşa in 1955, D: 36 cm.
- Roman period, 2nd cuntury A.D.Inv.No: A. 658

   Round plate with a beaded rim and flattened lip. The latter decorated with figures of lion, tiger, griffin, ante-lope and deer, each group separeted from one another by means of heads in profile within medallions and floral motifs, both in repoussé and incised. The tondo within incised concentric lines contains the head of Athena in high relief with crested Corinthian helmet, spear and shield, and an ægis with the head of Medusa on her chest. Hair falling loosely over the neck. Raised from a piece of silver plaque.

- Bronze Weight of Athena
- Found from Finike, H: 12.5 cm.
- Roman Period, 3nd century A.D.
  Inv.No: A.531

Steelyard weight in shape of a bust of Athena clad in a chiton, partly covered by an animal skin thrown over the left shoulder; a crested Corinthian helmet crowning the head. Hollow cast; filled with lead.

- Bronze Weight of Negro
- Found from Kapaklı in 1974
  H: 18 cm.
- Roman Period, 2nd century A.D.
  Inv.No:1.2.76.

Steelyard weight in shape of a bust of Negro. Upper part of body is naked. Hairs are deeply current. Face symbolised the type with thick lips and large eyes. Hollow cast, filled with lead.

- Baked clay Lamp
- Come from Dinar (Apameia),
  L: 9 cm.
- Roman Period, 3nd century A.D.
  Inv.No: A.305

Disk-shaped body with a protruding spout furnished with a wick hole. Convex discus decorated on top with alternating leaf and bead motifs in a ray pattern around the oil hole. Two opposing, double voluted knob handles around the rim; a mask in high relief between the body and the spout. Mould-cast.

- Baked clay Lamp
- Purchase, L: 10 cm.
- Roman Period, 3nd century A.D.
  Inv.No: A.871

Disk-shaped body with a protruding spout furnished with a wick hole. Flat discus decorated on top with a moulded relief of a crater with symetrically arranged wine branches and grapes descending from it. Oil hole placed off-center; another smaller hole between the body and the spout. Mould-cast.

- Bronze Lamp in shape of a Bull's Head
- Found in Arykanda (Arif) in 1984, L: 13.5 cm.
- Roman Period, 2 nd century A.D.
  Inv.No: 56.23.84

Bull's head with a vertically placed ribbon handle at the back. Projecting tongue with a wick hole; oil was poured into a cylindrical opening between the horns. Short hair on the forehead and between the horns, tube like ears. Cast.

- Bronze Figurine of Soldier
- Purchase in 1973
- H: 9.8 cm. Inv.No: 1.23.73
- Roman period, 3rd century A.D.

- Baked clay statuette of Aphrodite
- Purchase in 1975
- H: 28.5 cm. Inv.No: 2.15.75
- Roman period, 3rd century A.D.

- Baked clay Figurine of Eros
- Purchase in 1973
- H: 18.8 cm. Inv.No:3.57.73
- Roman period, 3rd century A.D.

- Bronze Figurine of Hermes
- Found-from Xanthos in 1984
- H:6.9 cm. Inv.No: A.671/1
- Roman period, 3rd century A.D.

- Baked clay Figurine of dressed Woman
- Found-from Patara in 1952
- H: 21.5 cm. Inv.No: A.600
- Roman period, 3rd century A.D.

- Marble Head of Zeus
- Found from Perge in 1979
- H: 13 cm.- . Inv.No:23.13.79
- Roman Period, 2nd century A.D.

The head broken at the neck below the chin is slightly tilted to the right and is crowned by thick, dissolved masses of curls. Bearded face with furrowed forehead and eyebrows indicated by fine chiseling, deep set eyes and slightly open mouth. A running drill was used to create the luxuriant and abundant locks of hair and beard.

- Marble Statuette of Tyche
- Found-from Seleukeia in 1953
- H: 38 cm. Inv.No: A.649
- Roman period, 2nd century A.D.

- Marble Statuette of Aphrodite
- Purchase in 1963
- H: 35 cm. Inv.No: A.1008
- Roman period, 2nd century A.D.

- Marble Statuette of Aphrodite
- Found-from Seleukeia in 1953
- H: 34 cm. Inv.No: A.648
- Roman period, 2nd century A.D.

- Marble Head of Serapis
- Found from Perge, H: 12.5 cm.
- Fine-graind white marble
- Roman Period, 3rd century A.D. Inv.No: 3.54.73

Head of Serapis with an oval face, tilted slightly to the left. Face with pronounced pupils, straight nose and thick lips framed by snail-like curls falling down loosely over the shoulders. Broken below the base of the neck.

- Marble Head of Athena
- Found from Perge in 1981
- H: 18 cm. - Inv.No:18.29.81
- Roman Period, 2nd century A.D.

The head broken at the neck. Eyebrows indicated by fine chiseling, deep set eyes and slightly open mouth. A crested Corinthian helmed crowing the head.

- Statue of Marsyas
- Found in Perge 1981 at the Gallery of Klaudius Peison (İ-7) of the South Bath
- Fine-grained white marble. H.2.00 m. (6 ft. 7 in.) Inv. No:5.29.81

The statue of Marsyas was discovered in 1981 in the Gallery of Klaudius Peison in the South Bath of Perge. It was broken into 16 fragments and restored. The statue is one of a group of three that were found in the area that relate to the musical contest between Apollo and Marsyas. He is represented as a naked-tall man. The weight of the body rests on the right leg and that the left leg was relaxed and extended forward. The lion pelt that covers the athletic shoulders of Marsyas is draped over the left arm with two claws hanging down and the tail reaching the base of the statue. At his right side is a tree trunk on which hangs the flute of Marsyas with its ten pipes. The inscription at the base announces that the statue was donated by Klaudius Peison. The origin of this Perge group is generally agreed to have been executed at the beginning of the 3rd cent. B.C. during the first Hellenistic Period.

Underwater section and Amphorai

THE GALLERY OF THE EMPERORS (Hall VI)

Hall Number 6 is dominated by a magnificent statue-the statue of a dancer dated to the second half of the second century A.D. Recovered during the excavations in Perge. This statue of a dancer is today the most impressive statue in the Antalya Museum. The whirling motion of her body and the chiton she wears reveal the contours of her body. The himation rolled into a belt gathers motion in its end points. Her hands hold the ends of her skirt and the neck is turned in a swift motion. The sculptor has used white marble for the body and black marble for the hair and garments.

In the same hall, behind the dancer, in a characteristic pose, is a group statue of the Three Graces (the Charites)-Aglaia (brilliance), Euphrosyne (joy), and Thalia, (bloom) who in mythology attended the feasts of the Olympian gods as well as those of mortals. In this group statue, two of the Graces are shown facing the front while the third in the center, faces the back. They hold each other by the shoulders.

Hall Number 6 is also known as the Gallery of the Emperors or the Gallery of the Royal Family because it contains some fine statues of Trajan, Hadrian, and Septimius Severus, the most famous Roman Emperors of the second and third century A.D. In their statues the emperors are depicted wearing their military out-fits; over their short tunics they wear their armor and their military cloaks, the paludamenta. The armors are decorated with the reliefs of two griffons standing opposite one another. The facial features of these statues bear personal characteristics.

Thanks to these statues, it is now fair that there had been a creative sculptor scholl which ignored official samples at figuring portraits of royal family in 2nd century A.D. in Perge.

The scholl is caracterized with its radical detail lining on statues. The way of lining, appearent in face and hair, come up in armor figuring as well.

The hair styles and the double layer of robes comprising a chiton and a himation as shown on the statues of Sabina, the Emperor Hadrian's wife, the Empress Faustina, the Younger, the wife of Marcus Aurelius, as well as the statue of the Empress Julia Domna, the wife of Septimius Severus and the mother of Caracalla and Geta, reflect the fashion of the Roman era.

Perhaps to most interesting statues of the hall are the statue of a noble lady by the name of Plancia Magna. A leading Pergaean of the second century A.D., Plancia Magna served in many offices: she was a priestess of Artemis as well as a priestess of the mother goddess Cybele. She was also a "demiourgos" or the highest civil servant of the city. As a generous donor, she presented Perge with a number of statues depicting various members of the Roman Imperial House circa 120 A.D. In her statues Plancia Magna is shown wearing a chiton over which she has a himation that also partially covers her head. Her hair which is parted in the middle is decorated with a crown adorned with the busts of emperors. Unfortunately the heads of these busts are missing.

These statues in the Hall of the Emperors are unique in that they portray the characteristics of the Roman portrait-sculptures and reflect the personal styles of the Pergaean artists.

In the niches across from the Hall of the Emperors there are the statues of Hera (Ephesian Type), a Priest of Apollo, Two Women, an Imperial Priest, a Priestess of Artemis. On the head of the Imperial Priest there is a crown adorned with the busts of the emperors whose heads are missing. The priestess of Artemis is shown with four rows of necklaces much like their present counterparts.

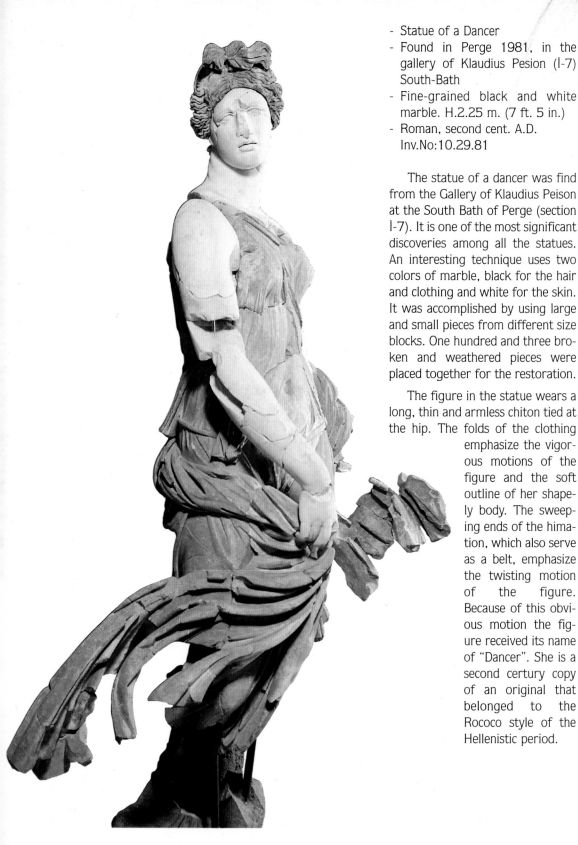

- Statue of a Dancer
- Found in Perge 1981, in the gallery of Klaudius Pesion (İ-7) South-Bath
- Fine-grained black and white marble. H.2.25 m. (7 ft. 5 in.)
- Roman, second cent. A.D. Inv.No:10.29.81

The statue of a dancer was find from the Gallery of Klaudius Peison at the South Bath of Perge (section İ-7). It is one of the most significant discoveries among all the statues. An interesting technique uses two colors of marble, black for the hair and clothing and white for the skin. It was accomplished by using large and small pieces from different size blocks. One hundred and three broken and weathered pieces were placed together for the restoration.

The figure in the statue wears a long, thin and armless chiton tied at the hip. The folds of the clothing emphasize the vigorous motions of the figure and the soft outline of her shapely body. The sweeping ends of the himation, which also serve as a belt, emphasize the twisting motion of the figure. Because of this obvious motion the figure received its name of "Dancer". She is a second century copy of an original that belonged to the Rococo style of the Hellenistic period.

- Statues of the three Graces (Charities)
- Found in Perge 1981(head) and 1982 (figures),section İ-8 of the South-Bath
- Fine-grained white marble. H.1.79 m. (5 ft. 10 in.)
- Roman, second cent. A.D. (Antonine period) - Inv.No:4.22.82

Aglaia (brilliance), Euphrosyne (joy) and Thalia (bloom); this satatues of three Graces was a magnificent find from section İ-8 of the South-Bath of Perge. This group is of greaf importance because no other replica of these famous Hellenistic originals exist either in Perge or the entire country. The head of the left figure was found during the excavation in 1981, the other figures were discovered a year later. The statue was reassembled from many broken pieces of fine grained white marble. The left and right figure of the group show a front view, while the middle one faces opposite, showing her back and putting her arms around the shoulders of the outside figures. Supports in the back of the statues are shaped like vases and covered with a cloth decorated with tassels. They reach from hip height of the figures down to the base. The style and technique dates this piece of art to the last half of the second century A.D. (Antonine period), based on originals of the Hellenistic period.

- Statue of Emperor Trajan
- Found in Perge 1979, the North portico of the palaestra in South-Bath
- Fine-grained white marble. H. 2.48 m. (8 ft. 2 in.)
- Roman, second cent. A.D. Inv.No:11.13.79

This statue features Trajan clad in armor richly decorated with relief ornament. It was discovered at Perge in 1979, during excavations of the Hellenistic wall near the North Portico of the Palaestra in the South Bath. Several fragments were fit together to construct the statue. Except for missing hands, the statue is in good condition. The weight of the body is supported on the right leg. The left leg is bent at the knee and extended to the side and back. Trajan is portrayed in all his dignity wearing a wreath on his head to emphasize his victorious return march from Dacia. Next to him sits a Dacian prisoner of war. Lion heads and eagles decorate the Pterygs, the rounded panels at the bottom of the armor. The head of Medusa decorates the center of his armor. Below this are two griffons. The lower part of his legs are protected with two rows of fringed leather straps. The same kind of straps can be seen around his arms. A paludamentum is affixed to his shoulder. His head is turned slightly to the side and upward. The head is intact except for a broken nose tip. The head appears to have been turned slightly to the right. The running-drill has very extensively and skilfully used in both the hair and the-crown. Locks of hair extend below the crown to decorate his forehead. The facial expression is typical of the emperor Trajan.

- Statue of Emperor Hadrian
- Found in Perge 1970 and 1971, in the Northern Monumental Nymphaeum
- Fine-grained white marble. H. 2.40 m. (7 ft. 10 in.)
- Roman, second cent. A.D. Inv.No: A-3738, A-3875

Hadrian's statue shows him clad in armor. It was discovered in 1970 and 1971, during excavations of the North Monumental Nymphaeum. His torso was discovered in 1970, broken into several pieces. The pieces of different sizes. His head was discovered a year later, broken in two pieces were fitted together at each break into a complete statue. Except for the missing right hand and the sword in left hand, the statue is complete. It is the best preserved example of Hadrian in this museum.

Over his tunic the emperor wears a carefully crafted armor shaped to the contours of his body. The weight of the body is supported on the right leg. The left leg is bent at the knee and extended to the side and back. The bottom portion of the armor has a row of rounded panels called pterygs. A paludamentum is affixed to his right shoulder. In the center of the armor is a head of Medusa with two griffons below. Two large bows secure a cingulum belt tied around his waist crossing the griffons. His legs are decorated with two protective rows of leather straps, fringed at the ends. These can also be noticed around his arms. His powerful head is crowned with a tall wreath of oak leaves. His face, framed with curls and a full beard, is raised slightly and turned to the left. The running-drill has been very extensively and skilfully used in both the hair and the crown. The Perge sculptor remained true to the official portrait by emphasizing all the characteristic facial expressions of Hadrian including his nose. The details of the face are well preserved.

- The Naked Statue of Emperor Hadrian
- Found in Perge 1971, in the Northern Monumental Nymphaeum
- Fine-grained white marble. H.1.42 m. (4 ft. 8 in.)
- Roman, second cent. A.D. Inv. No: A-3861, A-3863

The heroic naked statue of Hadrian was find during excavations in 1971 at the Monumental Nymphaeum of Perge. The statue was assembled from nine fragments. The lower thighs, a small piece of the neck, right hand and his penis are missing. There are several breaks in the paludamentum on his shoulder. The rest of the statue is in good condition. The emperor is depicted as a naked figure standing on his right leg while the left foot is partially set back. His right arm hangs down. His left arm is bent at the elbow and points forward where he holds a sword in his hand. The paludamentum is draped over his shoulder hangs and down his back. The bottom end is looped over his left forearm.

His head is tilted slightly upward and turned to the left. He is wearing a crown. His face is surrounded with wavy hair and curly beard. The running-drill has been very extensively and skilfully used in both the hair and crown. This representation of the emperor is significant because it is similar to a fifth century B.C. famous statue of Diomedes, the Greek warrior in the Trojan war.

- Statue of Sabina
- Found in Perge 1954-1955, at the Monumental arch, north of the Hellenistic Gate
- Fine-grained white marble.
  H. 2.08 m. (6 ft. 10 in.)
- Roman, second cent. A.D.
  Inv.No: A-3060, A-3086

Vibia Sabina, the wife of Hadrian, was the daughter of Mitidia as well as the grandniece of Trajan. She married Hadrian in 100 A.D. She accompanied her husband on most of his travels, but her marriage was very unhappy. She died in 137 A.D. and was deifled by Hadrian who had coins minted in her memory.

The head of Sabina's statue was discovered at Perge in 1954. The body was found in 1955 during excavations near the Monumental Arch North of the Hellenistic gate. Prof.Dr.Jale İnan discovered in 1963 that both pieces fit together. The right hand, parts of the left foot and much of the nose were broken off. The mouth, chin and area above the left eyebrow are chipped. There are areas of more damage on her body and especially on the cloth over her head. The statue of Sabina wears a himation over her chiton. The weight of the body rests on the right leg while the left leg is slightly bent at the knee and extended forwards and laterally. She is portrayed as a young woman. The head is decorated with a cresent shaped crown. Her hair is parted in the middle and combed back in wares around the side. Her hair is tied in a knot at the back, exposing her earlobes. The statue has all of the characteristics of a type of the "Great Herculanean." There is no doubt that it represents Sabina, for the statue was found near the pedestal inscribed "Sabina Augusta." Also a positive comparison can be made with her representation on coins and other portraits. This Sabina is portrayed a facial expression that is idealized even more than other portraits of her.

Both statues of Sabina and her husband Hadrian were discovered during the same excavation campaign. They were found close together and probably decorated the same monument. In addition the statues show the same stylistic characteristics. Therefore we can assign the same date of 121 A.D. to the statue of Sabina as for Hadrian.

- Statue of A Priestess of Artemis
- Found in Perge 1968-1969, near the Propylon of the South-Bath
- Fine-grained white marble. H. 1.68 m. (5 ft. 6 in.)
- Roman(Hadrianic) second cent. A.D. Inv.No: A-3280, 3456

Considering that Artemis was the chief goddess of Perge, the religious ceremonies, feasts and celebrations in her honor would have been most impressive. To achieve such high standards was the responsibility of the Artemis priestesses, who were treated as special people with special privileges in that city. Their importance is known by the fact that their statues were treated like symbols of the goddess. That is true of this statue. The head of the priestess was found in 1968 and the torso in 1969 near the propylon of the South Bath of Perge. The torso was broken in two pieces above the knee. Except for the two missing hands and a broken nose the statue is in good condition.The weight of the body rests on the left leg and on this side the line of the hips forms a strongly protruding curve. The priestess wears a chiton beneath a long himation. The chiton was worn as a veil over her head. It frames her forehead and her oval face so that no hair is visible. The chiton was tied below her chest. She wears five rows of necklaces around her neck; jewelry that reminds one of present day costume jewelry. A separate shell is suspended from her neck to below the waistline. The statue corresponds to those produced in Hadrian's time.

- Statue of A Priest of the Emperor Cult
- Found in Perge 1972, in the west portico of the Agora
- Fine-grained white marble. H. 2.03 m. (6 ft. 8 in.)
- Roman, second cent. A.D. (Early Antonine period) Inv.No:10.23.72

This admirable statue represents a bearded priest of the emperor cult. It has all the characteristics of other statues of priests found in Asia Minor and is one of the best of its kind. He in dressed in a chiton and himation like most statues of philosophers. He is standing on his left leg. His right leg is set slightly forward. His left hand wears a ring with an oval shield. His fingers hold onto the himation. He wears sandals with leather straps on his feet. Typical of priests of the emperor cult, he wears a band with emperor busts on his head. The band consists of a strophion with a ring, decorated with a wide band on which seven busts of emperors slightly damaged are attached. Short straight hair rests on his forehead. His face is wide and square with a moustache engraved by a drill. The hairstyle and beard remind one of the time of Hadrian, but the statue belongs more to the era of 140 A.D.

THE HALL OF THE SARCOPHAGI (Hall VII)

Some of the best sarcophagi of the necropolis, or burial grounds of Perge are displayed in this hall. At the entrance there is the striking columnar sarcophagus of Domitias Philiskas (third century A.D.). It has a flat lid in the Sidemara style in the shape of a couch. In the front, seated figures of two nude children decorate the corners of the lid. The deceased couple is shown reclining on top of the lid. The sides of the sarcophagus itself are decorated in high relief with standing or seated male and female figures. There is also an inscription bearing the name of the deceased. On one end of the sarcophagus is a false door in relief which is presumably one of the gates to Hades. A sacrifical altar and the sacred fire flanked by two figures are shown before this gate.

Reliefs of the twelve labors of Hercules decorate two sarcophagi of the second century A.D. The first sarcophagus has a gable-shaped lid. Each pediment is decorated with floral acroteria at three corners. There is a head of Medusa in the center. The roof tiles with antefixes are in the shape of lion heads. Along three sides, the sarcophagus proper is divided into panels by means of twisted columns with Corinthian capitals. Within the panels, the twelve labors of Hercules are represented in high relief. On the first of the two long sides of the sarcophagus there are the scenes of killing of the Nemean lion, the capture of the wild boar of Erymanthos, the Ceryneian hind, and the Stymphalian brids. On the first end, the cleaning of the Augean stables and the Hesperides'bringing the golden apples are depicted. On the second longer side of the sarcophagus, Hercules is depicted in combat with the Cretan bull. Scenes that follow depict the stealing of the horses of the Diomedes, the defeat of the Amazons, the killing of Geryoneus, and the capture of the dog Cerberus. On the second end of the sarcophagus, the relief of a false door, presumably one of the gates to Hades, shows the gate guarded by the Dioscuroi.

The second sarcophagus which is without columns also shows the labors of Hercules in twelve friezes. A sculpture from one of these friezes was exported illegally to the United States and later returned to Turkey by the Paul Getty Museum.

Other three sarcophai in the hall are the ones with garlands, all from Perge. Besides indicating the traditional sarcophagus decoration of the region they also express the huge dimention of historical trace trade. The bigger one has been transfered legally from Boston Broklyn Museum by Ministry of Culture. This sarcophagus with garlands, uncovered by illegal attempts in Antalya region and then smuggled out of the country between the years of 1985 and 1986 had been on exhibition in Brooklyn Museum, USA. Only after the initiatives of The Ministry of Culture has it been replaced to where it has ever belonged by December 1994. The smaller but an identical one has very well become an evidence for the bigger to be forwarded. The last is the sarcophagus rescued just before it was hauled by the smugglers.

Another sarcophagus entitled the "madallion" type of sarcophagus has sides decorated with winged figures supporting the head of Medusa. Along the sides of this sarcophagus there are a number of funerary urns and cinerary chest with Garlands.

Along another wall are displays of fragments of sarcophagi, one of which depicts a scene from The Iliad. In the foreground Priam demands the body of his son Hector from Achilles. In the background stand Helen and Hermes. This particular fragment was one of the first acquisitions of the museum.

At the rear of Hall Number 7 is a primitive Lycian votive stele dedicated to the Twelve Gods of Lycia. On the upper portion of this stele there are twelve armed figures below which there is a row of twelve styised dogs.

Among the grave stones in this hall, the newest and most exhilarating is, undoubtedly, the one for mime player Eucharistos of Patara.

A poetic inscription of 15 lines, uncovered by the excavations in 1989,   inspires a dialogue between a father and a son.

In the upper half of the stele is Eucharistos, illustrated bald and huge eyed.

The most impressive block in the hall, without doubt, is the Gaius Caesar relief, brought from the Cenotaph of Limyra.

Limyra, being one of the most important 6 cities of Lycia, literally "Zenuri" in Lycian, is located within the borders of Village of Yuvalılar of where is now Finike.

Gaius Caesar's Cenotaph is the one, found as a master piece of the excavations, held by Prof.J.Borchhard to the name of University of Vienna since 1968. The consturuction itself has a distinctive place among pyramid domed (monuments) as well as exposing outstanding importance for sculptor.

Now The Antalya Museum has caught the chance of possessing a relief with the block, brought by specialists of the museum in 1992 winter which we believe is not inferior to the ones decorating Ara - Pacis, one of the monuments from Augustus period in Rome.

1.90 x 0.90 m. sized block, illustrating horses with tense heads, seemingly hurtling themselves out of the block and Gaius Caesar and commanders with serene lookings, unarmed for the peace talks, all represent floriously the realistic appoach of sculptural works of Augustus period.

- Sarcophagus of Domitias-Filiskas
- Found in 1963, from the Eastern Necropolis of Perge
- Fine-grained with marble - L: 2.56 m. W:1.20 m.
- Roman Period, end of 2nd century A.D. Inv.No: A.929

Sarcophagus with a flat lid in shape of kline. At the front, seated figures of two naked children (Erotes) decorate the corners of the lid whereas the deceased couple is shown reclining on top. Sarcophagus proper is decorated with standing and seated male and female figures in high relief along the long sides and contains an inscription with the name of the deceased. A false door in relief, presumably one of the gates to Hades, behind a sacrificial altar and sacred fire flanked by two figures on one of the short sides.

- Sarcophagus of Hercules
- Found in 1963, from the Eastern Necropolis of Perge
- Fine-grained white marble - L: 1.65 m. W: 1.17 m.
- Roman Period, end of 2nd century A.D. Inv.No: A.928

    Sarcophagus with a gable-shaped lid, each pediment decorated with floral akroteria at three corners and a central Medusa head en face. Roof tiles with antefixes in the shape of lion heads Sarcophagus proper divided into panels by twisted columns with Corinthian capitals along three sides. Within the panels the "Twelve Labors of Hercules" are represented in high relief. A false door in relief, presumably one of the gates to Hades, guarded by the Dioskuroi is shown on one of the short sides of the sarcophageus.

- Sarcophagus with Hercules Reliefs
- Found in 1979 from the Roman necropolis of Perge
- Fine-grained white marble
- Roman period end of 2nd century. A.D. Inv.No: 1.11.81

    This sarcophagus with Hercules reliefs uncovered by illegal attempts in Perge and rescued just before it was hauled by the smugglers. It also shows the labors of Hercules in twelve free friezes. A sculpture from one of these friezes was exported illegally to the USA and later returned to Turkey by the Paul Getty Museum.

- Sarcophagus with Medallions
- Found in 1947, from the Western Necropolis of Perge
- Fine-grained white marble - L: 1.91 m. H: 0.78 m.
- Roman Period, end of 2nd century A.D. Inv.No: A.380

   Sarcophagus with a gable-shaped lid, each pediment decorated with floral akroteria at three corners and a round boss in the center. Roof tiles with antefixes in shape of lion heads sarcophagus proper decorated with a medallion containing the head of Medusa en face between two flying Erotes on one long side and two flying Nikai on the other. Single medallions with heads of Medusa en face on both ends.

- Sarcophagus with Garlands
- Found in 1994 from the Necropolis of Perge
- Fine-grained white marble, L: 220 cm. H: 100 cm.
- Roman Period end of 2nd century A.D. Inv.No: 1.68.94

This sarcophagus with garlands, uncovered by illegal ways in Antalya region and smuggled out of the country between the years of 1985-86 was exhibited in Brooklyn Museum, USA. Only after the initiatives of Turkish Ministry of Culture it has been placed to where it has ever belonged by december 1994.

- Sarcophagus with Mask reliefs
- Found in 1995 from the necropolis of Perge
- Fine-grained white marble
- Roman period end of 2nd century. A.D. Inv.No: 10.30.95

This sarcophagus with mask reliefs uncovered by illegal attemps in Perge and rescued just before it was hauled by the smugglers.

- Cinerary Chest with Garlands
- Found in 1963, from the Roman Necropolis of Perge
- Fine-grained white marble - L: 0.65 m. H: 0.39 m.
- Roman Period, end of 2nd century A.D. Inv.No: A.950

Composed of a gable-shaped lid decorated with floral akroteria at three corners of low pediments with central bosses on top of a chest proper. Roof tiles with antefixes in the shape of human heads en face. Thick garlands of oak-leaf surround all four sides of chest proper carried by Nikai at corners and by Erotes in the center of long sides. Within the garlands masks along the long sides, heads of Medusa en face on the short sides. Richly ornamented base moulding.

- Lycian Votive Stele
- Found in 1928, fromAntiphellos (Kaş)
- Limestone - L: 0.6 m. W: 0.34 m.
- Roman Period, late 3rd century A.D. Inv.No: A.169

Relief from Lycia dedicated to the Twelve Gods of Lycia, composed of two registers in high relief. Upper register contains twelve identical figures in two groups of six with a central figure framed in a niche. The fifth and sixth figures on the right partially preserved. Each figure, dressed in knee-length tunic faces frontward and holds a square shield. Lower register composed of a smaller central figure, presumably the dedicant, standing on a pedestal and flanked by twelve seated dogs in two groups of six; part of the fourth, fifth and sixth figures missing. The presence of shields and dogs may indicate that the figures are hunting deities. On a plain band between two registers the dedicatory inscription reads: "to Artemis, to the Twelve Gods and to their father".

- Frieze Block from the Cenotaph of Gaius Caesar
- Found in 1992, from Limyra (Finike-Yuvalılar köyü)
- Fine-grained white marble. H.1.90 m.- L: 90 m.
- Roman Period, 1st century A.D.Inv. No: 1.15.92

CENOTAPH: Is the name given to a burial monument which does not contain the body of the deceased, but killed on a foreign battlefield or at sea.

Starting with the Hellenistic and Roman eras both written evidence and actual examples of excavated cenotaphs exist. Following the spread of Christianity, some cenotaphs could be seen in churches.

In the works of ancient writers such as Herodotos, Thucydides and Pausanias, mention is made of cenotaphs erected in honour of Kings and heroes. Most of these resemble monumental tombs, and like other graves, contain the personal belongings and gifts of the deceased. In some cases, in place of the dead person, a large stone block was erected near which offerings were placed. Quite a number have steles on which are inscribed the names of heroes fallen in battle.

During excavations, urns have been found which contained neither bones nor ashes, and these have been described as cenotaphs. A very interesting example is the grave found in Locri in S. Italy where the cremation vessel instead of ashes and bones, was found to contain a female bust made of baked clay.

The cenotaph in Limyra was erected in honour of Augustus' grandson and adopted son Gaius Caesar. He was one of two sons born to Augustus' daughter Julia and her lover the consul Agrippa. In the year 2 B.C. the two brothers, Lucius and Gaius, were adopted by their grand-father Augustus and were proclaimed "Principes Juventutis" (principal heirs to the throne). However, neither brother was to become emperor. In the year 2 A.D. Lucius died during the Spanish campaign. Between the years 1 B.C. and 2 A.D. Gaius made a successful deal in Parthia. With him, at that time was Velleius Paterculus, who served on the military tribunal and who gave the following account of Gaius life there in his work entitled "Historia Romana".

According to Velleius, Gaius met the King of Parth on an Island on the Euphrates and came to an agreement with him. Later, on the return via north and while the city of Artagira was surrounded, Gauis was wounded by someone called Addius. As a result of this injury Gauis' mental and physical faculties were impaired and this state was made worse because of the high-ranking syncophants surrounding him. Shortly after this Gaius renounced his princedom, and although he wanted to live as an ordinary Roman citizen in the East, on the insistence of Augustus he set off for Rome. In the year 4 A.D. while on the return journey, he fell ill in Limyra, and died at an early age on 21 February. On Augustus' command his body was brought back to Rome by a military unit, and like his brother Lucius he was buried in Augustus' mausoleum. The people of Limyra, having obtained permission from the Roman senate, erected a magnificent cenotaph in his honor.

During the digs in Limyra betveen 1971-74 the remains of a cenotaph were excavated. This was on a square base with three steps leading up to a cubic-shaped edifice surrounded by pillars and, very probably like those in Anatolia, had a pyramid-shaped roof. As during the Byzantine era it was not observed as a cenotaph, it had suffered a lot of damage.

The cubic edifice on its limestone base was called an "Opus Caementitium Roman Cement", as it was consructed of rubble and plaster. The interior did not contain a chamber for the dead. From the remaining cavities it can be deduced that the exterior had been covered in marble. A marble frieze of a total 64 m. long and 2.20 cm. high surrounded the edifice.

Although during excavations only a small part of the frieze was found, a section depicting a big scene was discovered in the gardens of a hot-house owner in Limyra and was taken to the museum. This frieze depicts Gaius' eastern campaign and his meeting with the King of Parth among other events and the figures are life-size. The architectural remains found reflect the Augustus era. The remains of an inscription, which was probably in the architrave under the pyramidal roof, were also recovered, and recounted Gaius' succesful eastern campaign.

As this edifice, which was enclosed by sacred ground (temenos), was accepted as part of the Emperor cult, it is believed this was positioned in a South- easterly direction pointing to the Sirius star which relates to Gaius Caesar's date of birth in the second week in July.

The block in the Antalya Museum with a most significant frieze samples sculptural works in Augustus period of Anatolia.

- Grave-Stele of the Mime Player Eucharistos From Patara
- Found in 1989, from the Roman Necropolis of Patara
- Limestone - L: 67 cm. M:42 cm. W: 12 cm.
- Roman Period, mid of the 2nd century A.D.
  Inv.No: 1.29.89

During excavations at Patara in 1989 campaign, a grave-stele said to belong to the mime player (mimos) was unearthed.

The stele portrays the player both pictorally and poetically, showing him imitating the bald-headed mimos.

This traditional art has been kept alive in Anatolia until today by showings such as Hacivat-Karagöz (tradational Turkish shadow theatre), Kavuklu-Pişekar (principal characters of old Turkish theatre), tuluat (improvisations) and meddah (a public story-teller by using local tongues)

The well-known-characters in these showings are all bald. The poem imitated by mimos is a dialogue between father and son:

(FATHER)   YOU, WITH YOU LANGUAGE INSPIRED BY FAIRIES,
                ARE THE DELICIOUS SOUND OF ASIA,
                THE FLOVER PRAISED BY HELLAS,
                A FRESH SAPLING OF LYCIA;
                YOU ARE AMIABLE, LOVABLE, THE BEST OF ALL THE MIMOS.

(SON)   THIS IS I WHO ALONE ON THE STAGE
                CAN IMITATE THE STORIES OF LIFE,
                AND BY MY ACTING AND WORDS
                LEAVE EVERYONE SPELLBOUND.

(FATHER)   EUCHARISTOS, MY SON, I HAD THIS DONE FOR EUCHARISTOS.

(SON)   AS ONE WHO HUMS PHILISTION'S STINGING SATIRE,
                I HAVE FREQUENTLY REPEATED HIS SATIRICAL SAYING:
                " HERE IN AFTER I AM SILENT: LIFE IS BUT A DEPT."

According to Philistion's philosophy "life is loaned to us, with interest, which is paid upon death."

110

- Frieze Fragment from Sarcophagus
- Found in 1927, from the city walls of Antalya
- Fine-grained with marble - H: 0.85 m. L: 0.65 m.
- Roman Period, 2nd century A.D. Inv.No: A.118

This depicts the scene related in Homer's Iliad of the King of Troy, Priam, being taken to Achilles by the god Hermes. The old king has come to beseech Achilles'permission to take home the dead body of his son Hector for burial. The words used by Priam to soften Achilles'heart are as follows:

"Most worshipful Achilles, think of your own father, who is the same age as I, and so has nothing but miserable old age ahead of him. No doubt his neighbours are oppressing him and there is nobody to save him from their depredations. Yet he has at least one consolation. While he knows that you're still alive, he can look forward day by day to seeing his beloved son come back from Troy."

Upon these words Achilles'eyes filled with tears, and lifting the old man up, pronounced words to honor him. He then had Hector's body prepared for burial and handed it to Priam who, filled with both sorrow and honorable joy, took his body back to the people of Troy.

THE GALLERY OF THE ICONS (Hall VIII)

Icon, or devotional image, was an exclusively Byzantine product which enjoyed considerable popularity from the 12th century A.D.onwards in Anatolia and adjacent regions and is still used in Christian Orthodox churches.

Unlike monumental decoration, the icon has no ornamental function; rather, it is something to be worshipped, has protective powers and is an object of personal piety to be venerated, presented to the sick and taken on journeys. In acts of devotion, the icon of a saint or an event is brought out on the appropriate feast day; it is incensed and carried in processions.

The figures painted on the icons in a technique called tempera on wood were made on the principle of likeness to the holly persons they represent.

The origins of the icon which played an important role in the evolution of Byzantine painting can be traced back to the Hellenistic tradition of Late Roman portraiture.

A long and narrow hall to the left of the Hall of Sarcophagi is devoted to icons from the various churches in and around Antalya, date from the nineteenth and twentieth centuries. On the left wall there is a series of icons narrating the life of Christ: the Nativity, the Presentation in the Temple, the Circumcision, the Teaching in the Temple. Healing the Blind Man, Speaking with a Woman of a Samaria, the Transfiguration, the Triumphant Entry into Jerusalem, the Last Supper, Washing the Feet of the Disciples, Bearing the Cross, the Crucifixion and Resurrection.

The most colourful icon in the exhibition hall is, of course, the one on the short wall, figuring Christ and 12 Apostles, Christ in the mid with 6 Apostles on both sides, heading Christ except for Judas in the second (row) heading vesus.

There are other icons that depict the Virgin and Child, the Evangelists, St. John the Baptist, and St. Nicholas of Myra.

A small reliquary containing some of the bones of St. Nicholas has a lid with a portrait of the saint painted on the inside. Along with this portrait, a nineteenth-century Bible with embossed silver plaque on the covers deserve special attention.

Also exhibited in the front section of the Gallery of the Icons is a portion of the sixth century A.D. treasure of Corydalla (present-day Kumluca).Some 110 km. South of Antalya, which attest the highly distinct workmanship of the Byzantine silversmiths. The trove which has been discovered by the villagers in the early 1960's contained exquisite silver pieces, some with gilding, such as liturgical dishes, engraved crosses, polycandelons, dining implements, repousse book covers and cencers, the finest of its kind ever found. The majority of these silver finds bear inscriptions naming a bishop Euthycianus and a monastery called Holy Sion, located north of Myra (Demre) ,the port from which the Apostle St. Paul sailed to Rome. Five control stamps on each silver implement permitted the precise dating of these objects to the 6th century, i.e. to 565-575.

However, over a hundred pieces from the Kumluca treasure have been smuggled out of the country after the looting and are now in possesion of the Center for Byzantine Studies at Dumbarton Oaks Washington D.C.Attempts to recover these objects and to facilitate their return to the Antalya Museum still do continue.

- ICON - THE ANNUNCIATION
- Tempera on wood -1.31 x 0.72 m.
- 19 th century-Antalya - Inv.No: 3.2.82

Virgin Mary is depicted seated in front of an arched building on the right. An angel approaching from stylized clouds on the left and holding a bunch of flowers in her left and blessing with the right. Border composed of branch motifs. Below left an inscription which reads: O Evangelismos tes Theotoku.

- ICON - THE NATIVITY
- Tempera on wood -0.56 x 0.45 m.
- 19 th century-Antalya - Inv.No:59.2.82

Baby Jesus Christ lying on the manger at the center flanked by the Virgin Mary, an angel and there shepherds on the right and by angel and three kings (Gasper, Melkior., Baltazar) on the left. In the background the entrance to a cave with a bull and a donkey. On the clouds above, twelve angels in two groups of six left and right. An inscription in the cave reads: He Gennesis To Christou.

116

- ICON - THE CIRCUMCISION
- Tempera on wood -0.56 x 0.42 m.
- 19 th century-Antalya - Inv.No:163.2.82

Christ lying naked on a table covered with a richly embroidered cloth in front of an arched gateway with columns. A priest holding a knife to His right and other figures carrting candles behind the table. To the left of Him, from left to right, are a priestess erossing her arms across her chest. Virgin Mary, Joseph with a scroll and a high priest holding a Holy Bible in his left and blessing with his right.

117

- ICON- CHRIST AND THE SAMARITAN WOMAN
- Tempera on wood -0.55 x 0.42 m.
- 19 th century-Antalya - Inv.No:20.2.82

Main composition depicted within an arched frame. Christ is seated before a well in the foreground with the woman from Samaria standing opposite Him. Landscape filled with trees and a city with two wer-ing buildings in the background. On the left group of twelve Apostles with Paulus and Petrus in the front row walking towards Christ.

- ICON - Healing of the Blind
- Tempera on wood - H: 57 cm. W: 38 cm.
- 19th cuntury, Antalya.Inv.No: 144.2.82

    Christ standing in the center and touching the right eye of a blind seated on a rock. On the right, two other blind men waiting for their turn; seven others standing behind Him. A settlement and a figure covering his face with both hands in the back-ground.

- ICON - THE LAST SUPPER
- Tempera on wood -o.56 x 0.38 m.
- 19 th century-Antalya - Inv.No:147.2.82

Apostles seated around a rectangular table flanking Christ in two groups of six; table laid with fish, bread and wine. Judas shown as a young man resting his head on christ's chest. Apostles Petrus and Paulus standing to the right and left of Him. The scene is completed by an imaginary building with a draperg slung between the tower-like storeys.

- ICON - CHRIST WASHING HIS DISCIPLES FEET
- Tempera on wood -0.56 x 0.42 m.
- 19 th century-Antalya - Inv.No: 28.2.82

Christ after the last supper washes feet of twelve Apostles waiting for their turns behind the wooden parapeth. Petrus in the front.

ΕΛΚΟΜΕΝΟΣ ΕΠΙ ΣΤΡΟΥ.

- ICON - CHRIST ON HIS WAY TO GOLGOTHA
- Tempera on wood -0.56 x 0.36 m.
- 19 th century-Antalya - Inv.No:148.2.82

In the foreground Christ down to his knees with the heavy wooden cross tied at his back in an instant of rest. Six armed soldiers carrting spears surrounding Him; the one at the left with his back to the viewer, holding the end of the rope tied around His waist, another soldier to His right helping Him with the cross.

- ICON - THE CRUCIFIXION
- Tempera on wood -0.23 x 0.20 m.
- 19 th century-Antalya - Inv.No:149.2.82

   Within an arched frame Christ is shown crucified with blood dripping from nailed hands and feet as well as from wounds on the body. Flanked by Virgin Mary on the left and st. John on the right. Blue background filled with stars; pendants hanging from the arched frame top. A marble altar with candlesticks in the foreground Gilt halos.

- ICON - TWO ANGELS AT CHRIST'S EMPTY GRAVE
- Tempera on wood -0.56 x 0.45 m.
- 19 th century - Antalya - Inv.No:50.2.82

Main composition within an arched frame composed of two angels seated at both ends of Christ's sepulchre containing His shroud; Virgin Mary, Mary Magdalene and other women carrying perfume bottles on the right. In the gilt background, meeting of Christ with Mary Magdalene in front of a town.

124

- ICON - ST NICHOLAS
- Tempera on wood -0.43 x 0.29 m.
- 19 th century-Myra (Demre)   Inv.No:160.2.82

   A frontal representation of the Saint in bishop's robes, seated on an elaborately carved, pillowed chair without back. In his left hand he holds an open Bible; his right is raised in blessing. Gilt halo.

☞ CENSER - Gilt silver with niello
6th century A.D. (Byzantine) - H.17 cm.
Korydalla (Kumluca) - A.1019

Censer with cylindrical body, ring base and suspension chains intact. Body decorated with a frieze in repousse, containing scenes from New Testament bordered at the bottom with a band of leaf patterns. Below the rim a plain band with a nielloed inscription; "To Virgin Mary, Mother of God, from Euthycianus most humble bishop". Five control stamps.

SILVER TRAY - Gilt silver with niello
6th century A.D. (Byzantine) -D: 60 cm.
Korydalla (Kumluca) - A.1020

Decorated flat tray with a ring base and four control stamps. In the center, a large chrismon within a band comprising an engraved and nielloed inscription: "To the Lord, for the salvation of Eutychianus, most humble bishop". Border composed of twenty-nine cups in repoussé in gilt medallions; flattened rim decorated with gilt leaf and egg-and-dart motifs repoussé. Raised from a piece of silver plaque.

☞ POLYCANDELON - Silver with niello
6th century A.D. (Byzantine) - D.56 cm.
Korydalla (Kumluca) - A.1054

Circular polycandelon designed for the suspension of twelve glass lamps. Decorated in openwork with a cruciform element in the center; each arm terminating in a circle flanked by two dolphins topped with smaller circles comprising inscribed cross monograms: two bear the name "Bishop", the other two "Euthvcianus". A circular concentric band with a nielloed inscription: "In fulfillment of a vow and for the salvation of Euthycianus, most humble bishop". Outer band decorated with four crosses, spirals and twelve round spaces for lamps. At the back four suspension loops.

THE GALLERY OF MOSAICS (Hall IX)

Leaving the Hall of Icons, the visitor comes to another large hall where some very fine but rather damaged mosaics from Seleuceia and Xanthos are exhibited.

The ancient city of Seleuceia from where the two large mosaics-dated back to 2nd cent.B.C. have come, is pronounced as Seleuceia of Pamphylia and located in 25 km. Northeast of the ancient city of Side.

Among the mosaics unearthed by Prof.Jale İNAN between the years of 1978 and 1979 in Seleuceia, there appears a large sample decorated with the portraits of Solon, Thucydides, Lycurgus, Herodotos, Hesiod and Demosthenes. Name "Homer" is in the center of the mosaic. One other mosaic from the same location flaunts Orpheus pretentiously among wild animals. Orpheus, in mythology is known to be the famous mythical poet, son of Eagrus and the Muse Calliope, who gave birth to him on the banks of the Hebrus in Thrace. Such was his power in song, that he could move trees and rocks and tame wild beasts thereby. When his wife, the Nymph Eurydice, died of a serpent's bite, he descended into the lower world, and so moved Persephone by the music of his song, that she permitted him to take Eurydice back with him to the upper world, on condition of his not looking round during his passage through the realm of the dead. In spite of this, his impatience led him to gaze back, and Eurydice had to return forever to Hades.

Among the mosaics from the large basilica of Xanthos, is one that depicts Thetis bathing her child, Achilles, in the River Styx to make him invulnerable.

Thetis, in mythology is know to be the daughter of Nereus and Doris, wife of Peleus, and mother of Achilles. On many occasions she proved herself of assistance to the gods. When Zeus was threatened by Hera, Athena and Poseidon, she called Briareus to his aid. When Hephaistus was cast out of heaven by Zeus, she took him and hid him for nine years.

Again, when Dionysos was fleeing before Lycurgus, she afforded his protection in the sea. Brought up by Hera, she was wooed by Zeus and Poseidon. But when Themis foretold that Thetis would bear a son who would be greater than his father, she was married against her will to amortal, Peleus. This marriage was the source of the greatest sorrow to her. Her attempt to make her only son Achilles immortal was frustrated by her husband, and caused an estrangement between them, and she was fated to see her glorious and godlike son cut of in the prime of life.

Another mosaic is decorated with the portraits of Eirene, the goddess of peace, and Euprepeia, the goddess of propriety. A third one shows the portraits of Atalanta and Meleagros hunting the Calydon boar. These mosaics date to the Byzantine Period.

Decorating the wall on the right is a second century A.D. disc with a relief of Artemis Pergæa and the sings of the Zodiac. There is also an excellent statue of Meleagros recovered from Perge. The visitor must particularly note a statue which archaeologists have painstakingly reconstructed from hundreds of small fragments unearthed at Letoon, near Xanthos. This statue was once a part of a shrine dedicated to Leto and her children, Artemis and Apollo. The shrine was demolished in ancient times.

Potraits, in relays on the same wall, are the ones that inspire the full attitude at art of portrait in Roman time. They not alone do reflect the progress in official imperial portraits, beard and hair style but they also impress the features of the art of portrait in the region.

Nearby, in the same hall, there is a sixth century pulpit decorated with a relief of the angel, Gabriel. It is interesting to note an inscription in the roundel on the bottom left, written in the Arabic script that reads "Allah".

The marble ambo parapeth and lime-stone corner fragment, next to the pulpit, Gabriel, is an outstanding sample to Byzantine period religious architecture.

On another wall, there are some tools used in making sculptures. There is also an unfinished block of marble and a male head of marble. An arm of a colossal bronze statue is also displayed here. In front of these artifacts is a large marble slab identified as a game board. The piece was found during the excavations of the Colonnaded Avenue of Perge. From the many similar examples recovered at different sites in the region one can deduce that such games were very popular in ancient times.

- Limestone Head of Apollo
- Found from Patara in 1952 H: 41 cm.
- Hellenistic Period 1st century B.C.
- Inv. No.: A. 603

- Statue of Meleagros
- Found in Perge 1981 at the Gallery of Klaudius Peison (İ-7) of the South Bath
- Fine-grained white marble.
  H. 2.07 m. (6 ft. 9 in.)
  Inv. No:9.29.81
- Roman,
  second cent. A.D.

The statue was discovered in 1981 during excavations in the Gallery of Klaudius Peison (Division İ-7) of the southern Bath of Perge. 47 broken pieces were found and pieces together. The hero is shown as a sad, but handsome athletic young man standing on a large base. The weight of the body is supported on the right leg, the left leg being relaxed, bent at the knee, and drawn back wards.

He is leaning against a lance with the head of a boar at his right side and a dog at his left. He is almost naked. A chlamys cloth is tied with a brooch at his right shoulder.

It goes around his neck and left arm and hangs down to the head of the boar. The original statue of Meleagros by the famous sculptor Skopas dates back to the fourth century B.C. This Roman copy dates to the second century A.D. and is dedicated by Klaudius Peison as indicated by the inscription on the base.

- Marble Relief of Archangel Gabriel
- Found in Antalya 1928, H: 100 cm. W: 89 cm.
- Byzantine period, 6th cuntury A.D. Inv.No: A . 156

Possibly part of an ambo parapet reused and recarved in different periods. A cross in high relief on the rear face. A half-figure representation of Archangel Gabriel in relief holding a medallion; an inscription bearing the name "Allah" carved in arabic on the medallion attests its use by the Turks in later periods. Becide exposing both historical and archaeological significance, the Gabriel block is exceptionally important as it has brought religious tolerance to our date.

136

- Limestone Ambo Parapet
- Purchase from Elmalı in 1973, H:73 cm. L: 125 cm. Th: 11 cm.
- Byzantine period, 6th cuntury A.D.Inv.No: 1.30.73

Composed of three convex, rectangular, figured panels separated by ornamental borders with incised lattice pattern. Each arched panel framed by two engaged columns topped with palmette capitals. Central panel depicts a frontal standing figure, presumably Jesus Christ; side panels contain winged angels with their right hands extended and holding a scroll in their left.

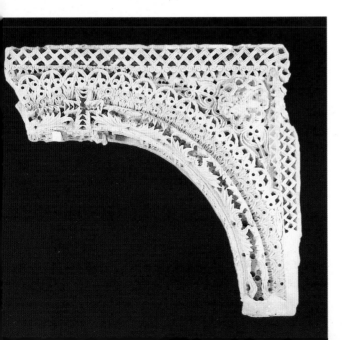

- Limestone Architectural Element
- Found in Pogla (Çomaklı) in 1981 H: 73 cm. L: 125 cm.
- Byzantine period, 6th cuntury A.D. Inv.No: 1.30.73

Fragment of a revetment plaque belonging to the corner of an arch. Framed with delicately carved diamond-pattern; intricate floral motifs along the straight and concave edges in openwork; concave face decorated with a row of rectangular cassettes in relief.

- Zodiac Disc with Pergæan Artemis
- Found in Perge, in 1977- D: 91.5 cm
- Fine-grained white Marble
- Roman period, 2nd century A.D. Inv.No: I.28.77

Disc surrounded by twelve sing of Zodiac, one sign broken. In the center, bust of Artemis with lunate projections on both shoulders, framed by relief figures of Atlas, river gods and a draped female to the left. Head of bust missing.

- Statue of the woman from Letoon
- Found in Letoon 1975-1977
- Fine-grained white marble.
  H: 2.03 m. (6 ft. 8 in.)
  Inv. No:1.18.77
- Hellenistic, second cent. B.C.

She is a young woman, dressed in tunic and himation. She stands on her left leg. Her right foot is silghtly turned to the side. One interesting aspect is that despite the many folds of her clothing, her body features stand out clearly. The long garment covers her legs so that only the tips of her toes and sandals are visible. The statue is the same style as the one in the theater at Magnesia and in the Celsus Library in Ephesus. All of these come from the sculptural school of Kos island, in the second century B.C.

- Statue of Hera Ephesia (Juno)
- Found in Aspendos, in museum since 1926
- Fine-grained white marble.
  H. 1.83 m. (6 ft.)
  Inv. No: A . 97
- Roman, second cent. A.D.

The statue of Hera was one the first to be brought from Aspendos to the Museum of Antalya. With the exception of her missing head, the right arm, and the left hand, her statue is complete and in good condition. The full weight of her body rests on her left leg while the right leg is set gracefully to the side. The goddess wears a long himation coat over a thin and transparent chiton (a woman's armless garment). Her left arm is apparently bent at the elbow and points toward the front,while the right arm hangs straight down. The standing figure as well as the flowing garment show the curves of her body clearly. These characteristics all conform to the style of an "Ephesia" type statue that traces back to the Ionia of the fifth centuryB.C. On the hem of her himation coat are engraved the names of two-sculptors: Moschos and Kallippos from Synnada (Afyon-Şuhut). The statue is also very similar to the replica in Vienna that gave this statue its name. So "Hera Ephesia" is the only statue in the museum that has the artist's name engraved on the garment.

- Marble Head of a Young Girl
- Found from Letoon in1977, H:38cm.
- Hellenistic Period, 2nd century B.C. Inv.No: 2.18.77

   The head with the base of its neck rounded for insertion into a statue is inclined forward a little and turned slightly to its left side. The face is a pointed oval with soft features: small "dreamy" eyes with lids in relief, and small, full-lipped mouth. The hair, parted in the middle, is sketchily rendered in large strands tied in a knot above the nape of the neck. The top of the head probably separately carved.Nose broken.

- Potrait Head of a Woman from Alacami Village of Serik
- Fine-grained white marble - H: 0.24 m.
- Roman Period, 3nd century A.D. Inv.No: A.1016

Head of a woman with hair parted in the middle and topped with an additional coiffure. Hair sketchily rendered by incision, narrow strands of hair join at the nape, leaving the ears uncovered. Arched nose, eyes with drilled pupils and tight-lipped mouth lend a sense of individuality to the face. Head broken below the chin; part of the chin chipped off.

- Potrait Head of a Man
- Fine-grained white marble - H: 0.22 m.
- Roman Period, 3rd century A.D. Inv.No: A.322

Head of a man with a bearded round face, short hair, furrowed forehead and a dimple on the chin. Beard, moustache and eyebrows indicated by deep incisions. The plastic rendering of the eye, marking the iris by an incised circle and the deepening of the pupil by drill holes, set into a crescent-shaped depression give the portrait a sense of individuality and emotional expression. Head broken above the base of the neck; right side of the nose with the tip chipped off.

CENTRAL COURTYARD

Many sculptural and architectural pieces dated back to different periods are exhibited in the central courtyard. Without any doubt, Limyra findings are the most significant pieces situated in this courtyard. These pieces have been unearthed by Prof. J.Borchhardt from Vienna University. They are from the Heroon of Lycian King Perikles, dated 4th century B.C. (Classical Period) and architectural pieces from the Ptolemaion which dated 2nd century B.C. (Hellenistic Period).

Becide of them small than life-size statues of Mousas "Nymphs of Inspration" and Inscripted bastion from the city walls of Antalya which dated 14th century A.D. (Seljuk Period) are also worth seeing, in this courtyard.

The Heroon of Perikles,
King of Lycia (370-358 B.C.)

The building is situated on a terrace (20x20 m.). The podium (hyposorion) can still be seen "in-situ" and included the tomb. The upper part of the Heroon looked like an amphrprostyle temple which was reserved for the cult

Instead of columns four Karyatides on each side were holding the entablature. The cella west-frieze showed Perikles as a charia-teer and his liege Atraxeres III, Great king of Persia riding a horse. The north akroteria symbolise Perseus triumphantly over the beheaded Medusa whose sisters Stheno and Euryale try to escape frightened.

146

North pediment of the monumental grave (heroon) of Perikle Limyra. Perseus is seen holding up the head of Medusa in his r hand.Limestone. 4th. Century B.C.

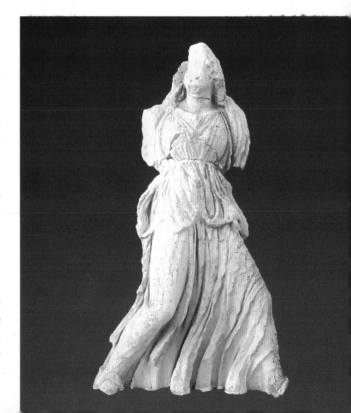

Model of the Heroon of King Perikles
Photo. F. Krinzinger

The Ptolemaion of Limyra

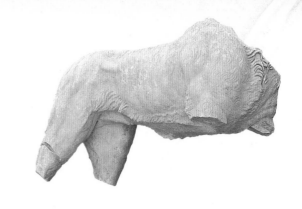

In the 3rd century B.C. the city of Limyra built this edifice dedicated for their rulers. A round construction surrounded by columns was set upon a square plinth. This round construction contained the approx. 2,70 m. high marble cult statues of the Ptolemaic ruling family.

The metope-triglyphe frieze around the plinth depicted subjects of Greek mythology such as the victory of the Lapithae over the Centaurs on the northern side. The corners of the plinth were guarded by splendid marble lions. The outer wall of the cella was adorned with a running frieze, showing chariot races, above the door and window apertures. A cone-shaped tile roof with a huge acroter with winding serpents crowned the round construction.

Lion - Lion Head and Kentauromachie frieces from the Ptolemaion. 3rd. Century B.C.

In mythology Muses were the Nymphs of inspirings springs, then goddesses of song in general, afterwards the representatives of the various kinds of poetry, arts, and sciences. In Homer, who now speaks of one, and now of many Muses, but without specifying their number or their names, they are considered as goddesses dwelling in Olympos, who at the meals of the gods sing sweetly to the lyre of Apollo, inspire the poet and prompt his song. They were nine daughters of Zeus and Mnemosyne, born in Pieria, and mentions their names, to which we shall at the same time add the province and the attributes afterwards assigned to each. (1) CALLIOPE (she of the fair voice), in Hesiod the noblest of all, the Muse of epic song; among her attributes are a wax tablet and a pencil.(2) CLIO (she that extols), the Muse of history; with a scroll. (3) EUTERPE (she that gladdens), the Muse of lyric song; with the double flute. (4) THALIA (she that flourishes), the Muse of comedy and bucolic poetry;with the comic mask, the ivy wreath, and the shepherd's staff. (5) MELPOMENE (she that sings), the Muse of tragedy; with tragic mask, ivy wreath, and occasionally with attributes of individual heroes, e.g. the club, the sword. (6) TERPSICHORE (she that rejoices in the dance), The Muse of dancing; with the lyre. (7) ERATO (the lovely one), the Muse of erotic poetry; with a smaller lyre. (8) POLYHMNIA (she that is rich in hymns); the Muse of serious sacred songs; usually represented as veiled and pensive. (9) URANIA (the heavenly), the Muse of astronomy; with the celstial globe.

MELPOMENE- The Muse of tragedy with tragic mask.

LIO- The Musa of History with a scroll.   POLYHYMNIA- The Muse of sacred songs.

- Inscripted Bastion from the fortress of Antalya
- Marble and limestone - H: 3.15 m. - W: 3.05 m.
- Seljuk Period, 13th century A.D. Inv.No: 2.12.91

Bastion in the form of a fountain with twisted columns, multifoil arch and pediment with thick tenons. Composed of thirty-two dressed blocks in six rows. Within the arch is an inscription of five lines in thick sülüs script starting with the words: "Emri bi imarı Hazel Burç", built by Keyhusrev bin Keykubat.

The building of this sacred fortress was ordered by Keyhüsrev, the son of Keykubad who was the son of Keyhüsrev, the master of nations, the guard of the horizons, and the shade of God in this world and in the other. In the year 642 = 1226 A.D.

THE HALL OF ANCIENT COINS AND JEWELRY (Hall X)

After leaving Hall Number Eight, the corridor leads the visitor to Hall Number 10 which contains the Museum's coin collections representative of the coins of the region. Coins from Pamphylia, Pisidia and Lycia are in the display cases on the left wall. The coins from the Hellenistic, Roman, Byzantine, Seljuk, and Ottoman Periods are, however, in the cases on the right wall. The central case in front of the wall opposite the entrance contains jewelry from the vicinity.

As the visitor proceeds along the left wall, the first case gives an explanation of minting tecniques. The second case contains sample coins from the Pamphylian cities of Attaleia, Perge, Madydus, Aspendos, Sillyon, and Side. The most interesting pieces in this second case are; the silver Aspendos Stater depicting a boy with a sling-shot on one side and two wrestlers on the other side (fourt century B.C.); the silver tetradrachma of Side depicting the head of Athena on one side, and Nike and a pomegranate on the other (Third century B.C.).The collection comprising the coins of about 25 cities of the region is displayed in chronological order starting from the coins of the Hellenistic Period and proceeding to the coins of the Roman Period.

A third show-case contains the coins of about twenty Lycian cities and six Lycian dynasties, displayed in chronological order from the Archaic Period to the end of the Roman Period.

The Silver stater, from the excavation of "Avşar Tepe" near the ancient city of Kyaneai, - held by parthership of Tübingen University and the Antalya Museum- is the latest and most atracting find of this section.

The stater, supposed to have belonged to the years 440-420 B.C., is highlighted as it has evi-

- Silver Stater from the hoard of Aspendos
- W: 10.9 gr. 375 - 350 B.C.

OBVERSE: Two naked wrestlers Between FA
REVERSE: Standing figure of a slinger in action to the right; a triskeles and a club. To left inscribed ΕΣFEDIY

- Silver Tetradrachm from the hoard of Side
- W: 16 gr. 247 - 180 B.C.

OBVERSE: Helmetted head of Athena to the right.
REVERSE: A Standing Nike holding a laurel- wreath, to the left; pomegranate and letters AR.

Aspendos

Side

Side

dential value to enlighten one of the oldest citys of the region by the name "SPPTNAZA" read on reverse.

The first case in front of the right wall displays a collection of coins from the Hellenistic Kingdoms; from the time of Alexander III (336-323 B.C.) to the time of Seleucos III (222-187 B.C.). The second show-case contains the coins from the Roman Empire, from the time of Augustus (27 B.C.-14 A.D.) to the time of Theodosius (379-395 A.D.)

In the case representing the Byzantine Period, there are the coins of the Byzantine Empire from the reign of Anastasius (491-518 A.D.) to the conquest of Istanbul, or Constantinopolis, by the Turks in 1453.

The collection of Ottoman coins ranges from the reign of Osman Bey, the founder of the Ottoman Empire (1299 A.D.), to the founding of the Republic of Turkey (1923). The collection contains the coins of 36 rulers over a period of 623 years. The display of the collection also includes the first banknotes issued during the last years of the Ottoman Empire.

As for the cases displaying various treasures, the visitor's eyes may feast on the treasures of silver unearthed in Aspendos and Side. There is also a treasure belonging to Probus, a Roman Emperor.

In the middle case gold, silver, and glass jewelry samples from the fourth century B.C. to the sixth century A.D. are exhibited. Gold and silver earrings, bracelets, necklaces, and strings of glass beads are some of the examples on display. A hoop earring with a bull's head showing fine filigree is an interesting piece dating back to the Hellenistic Period, 2nd century B.C.

- Silver Stater of from Lycia
- 440 - 420 B.C. 9.73 gr.
- OBVERSE: Head of Athena
- REVERSE: Tetraskeles - "SPPŇTAZA"

156

Golden Stater of Alaxander the
Great (336-323 B.C.)
King of Macedonia

Golden Nomisma
Constantine-X Ducas
(1059-1067) Byzantine Emperor.

Gold
Süleyman the Magnificent
Ottoman Emperor
1520-1566

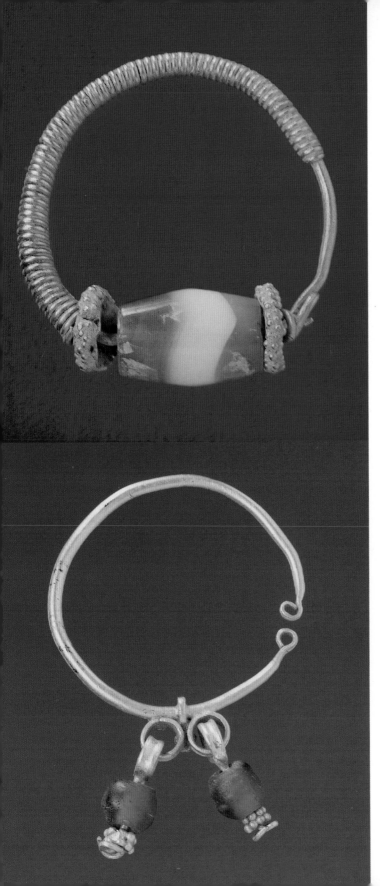

- Golden Earring (Purchase)
- L: 2.3 cm. W: 1.3 cm.
  Inv.No:46.3.79
- Roman Period, 2nd century A.D.

Hoop of gold with two pome-granate-shaped hollow beads suspending from a red stone pendant.

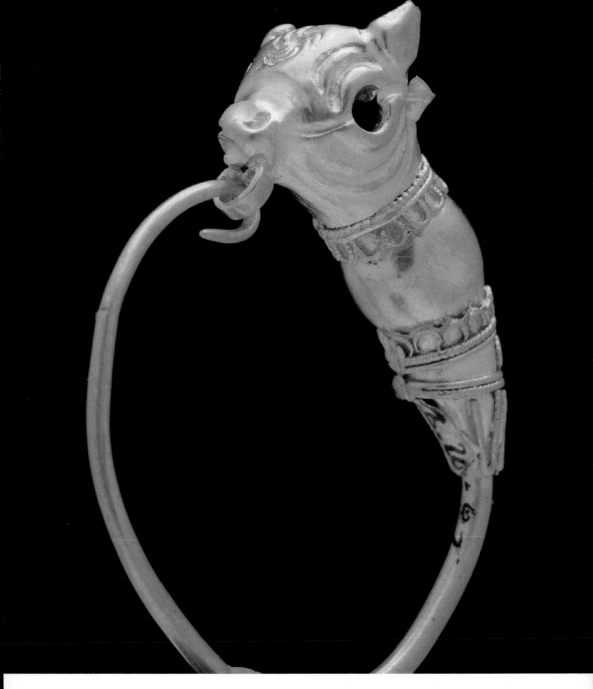

- Golden Earring from Antiphellos (Kaş)
- L: 2.5 cm. D: 2.8 cm. Wt: 41 gr.
- Hellenistic Period, 3rd century B.C.
  Inv.No: 3.20.87

    Hoop of gold, hooked on one end to fasten to a ring at the other beneath bull's head. Below the head, double collars decorated with circles in filigree. Eyes of the bull once inlaid, now lost.

ETHNOGRAPHICAL EXHIBITS (Halls XI, XII and XIII)

The Antalya Museum's ethnographical collection occupies three galleries of the present-day museum, namely the halls 11, 12 and 13.

(A. Naci Eren Hall) HALL NUMBER XI

Some very fine examples of Seljuk and Ottoman tiles, porcelain, religious materials, lamps, jewelry, seals, watches and medals are displayed in this hall.

The Seljuk tiles on display originally decorated the Aspendos theater, when the building used as a residence or caravansarai during the reign of Sultan Alaettin Keykubat I. These thirteenth century A.D. and mostly turquose, medium and deep blue tiles were made using underglaze technique with plant, human and animal motifs as well as inscriptions. The Ottoman tiles, on the other hand, present different samples from the fifteenth century to the eighteenth century. These tiles were made in the Iznik workshops as a main ceramic center of Ottoman period. The principal colors used in this period were red, green, cobalt blue, turquose and black; the favourite motifs cosisted of blossoming trees and flowers. The porcelain ware, however, is superior product of the factory of the Yıldız Palace in İstanbul, made in nineteenth century, by Sultan Abdulhamit II.

In 19th century; another Ottoman ceramic center was Çanakkale. This center especially known to have buf color plates with ship design in it. In the fourth show-case of this hall have been exhibiting some very fine decorated lamps which come late 19th and early 20th century.

The show-case housing cigarette and coffee sets display the fitnest materials related to cigarette-smoking and coffee-drinking that were important in the daily life of the Ottoman Period. Among the materials; coffee box, coffee mill, coffee bean cooler, coffee pan, cups end envelopes are the most eye-catching of all.

Among the religious materials presented in this hall, the most interesting item is a Koran from the Seljuk Period. The book comprieses 189 pages which are richly decorated with gilded geometric designs. Carved wooden Koran stand (rahle) is another important religious material for daily life of islamic people in mosques.

The watches; between medals and seals cases are some 38 pieces in the collection,acquired by the museum as gifts or by purchase, 16 watches are on display and include these of German, English, Italian an Swiss origin.

The costume collection of the museum includes women's traditional wear not only from the region but from various parts of Anatolia. The type known as the "Bindallı" is the most popular and the most eye-catching of all.

Baggy trousers, karchief, bundle wrappar and embroidered towels are another ethnological samples of the show-case.

In the case containing arms, the visitor can view a display showing the evolution of arms, from the bow and arrow to the pistol.

Seljuk Tile from the Stage building of the theatre at Aspendos. 13th cuntury A.D.

Composed of star-shaped underglaze-painted tiles decorated with floral motifs blackish blue on blue ground and small square tiles with bird, inscription and floral designs in cream on blue ground at four corners of each star-shaped tile.

Ottoman tiles from the İznik work- shops second half of 16th century A.D.

Underglaze painted tile with plum, artichoke and tulip flowers in coral red, green and cobalt blue on white ground.

- 19th century Plate
- From Çanakkale workshop

- Decorative Oil Lamps
- From late Ottoman Period (19th century).

- Coffee cups and envelops.

- Gold gilt paper The Holy Koran
- From Tekelioğlu Library - L: 31.3 m.-W: 24.5 m.
- Seljuk Period, 13th century A.D. Inv.No: 1.1.81.

Contains 189 pages and is bound in red leather. Opening folios illuminated in gold gilt, all other pages illuminated.

"Divit" Silver an inkholder and a pen-case.

HALL NUMBER XII

On the corridor leading one from Hall Number 11 to Hall Number 12, unusual examples of calligraphy scales and the religious materials from the Elmalı Abdal Musa Dervish Convent are displayed.

The art of callgraphy was one of the most favourite parts of Ottoman art.These hand written works mostly used for Koran, religious books and holy papers like "Hilye" or "Kelime-i Tevhid". The principal tools used in this art are the reed pen, a knife-like sharpener used to shape the pen, an inkholder and a pen-case known as "Divit". On completion, the handwritten works of the callgraphers were given to illuminators who embellished each page of writing with a gilded frame and added decorative motifs in gold which was called "Tezhip" along its edges.

This art indicates different sort of characters, most preferably the chracters of küfi, nesih, sülüs and taliyk. The first calligraphic work on the left wall of the hall is the "Kelime-i Tevhid" which means "The god is the only and Muhammad is the prophet". Second is the work "Hilye" which describes Muhammad. Artists, in Hilyes, arrange their work of Hilye in ten sections each of which initiates with "Bismillahirrahmanirrahim" (in the name of merciful and the god Allah) and is concluded with a florid decoration. It is believed in Islam that wherever a hilye shows, it brings protection and serenity. The final plates on the wall are the documents called "İcazed" (permission).

Traditional Women dress known as a **Bindallı** and ornaments. Belt, Belt Buckle, Head Ornament and Cap from Antalya Region.

Traditional Woman dress and clogs with inlaid mother-of Pearl from Antalya Region.

In the show-case containing spoons, the story of spoon-making from its designing stage to its actual making, is presented. The case also includes tools used for the purpose.

The case that displays musical instruments includes paticularly those instruments used by the nomads of the region. Both the case containing spoons and the case displaying musical instruments, represent samples of the handcraft of the people of Anatolia.

The most interesting corner of Hall Number 12 is the Yörük, or the nomads tent. A sample of the Black Tent used in the mountains in the summer time and by the seaside in winter, is displayed with all the related materials necessary in the daily life of the nomads.

The "Döşemealtı" Carpets native Antalya are the next most interesting objects of this hall. Döşemealtı is a name to a territory covering around 40 villages in Northeast of Antalya.This is the home to those nomadia characterized, small size carpets woven in 9 variety with dark colours dominating. Among these "HALELLİ" is the oldest and most traditional sample.

There are various rug samples and a loom on display in this hall. The small show-cases contain other samples of local weaving.

In the case that presents locks and keys the viewer has the opportunity to observe the evolution of locks and keys from their earliest wood examples to the present-day metal ones.

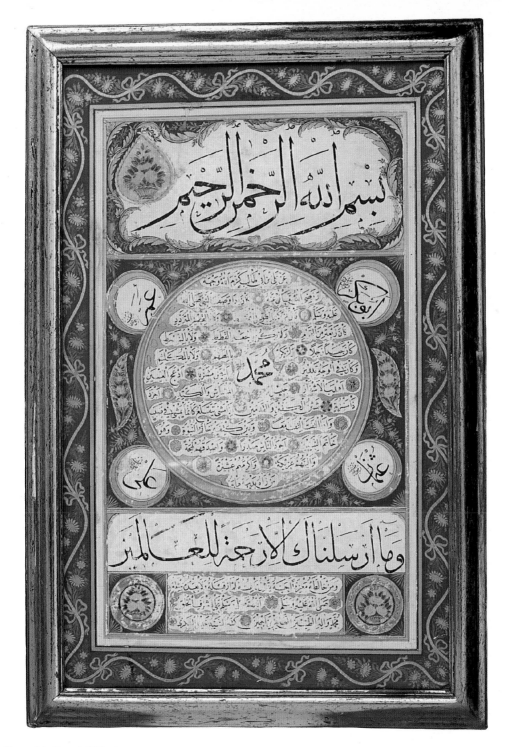

- Calligraphic Panel (Hilye)
- Paper - H:67cm. W:45cm.
- Ottoman Period, Alanya 1975

Comprising an illuminated prayer written in sülüs and nesih scripts within a rectangular frame. Executed by Seyit Halil Şükrü and dated to 1245 Hegria.(1829 A.D.)

- Calligraphic Panel (İcazetname)
- Paper - H: 30 cm. W: 37.5 cm.
- Ottoman Period, İstanbul 1972

  Composed of five lines of sülüs script within a rectangular blue frame. Executed by Muhammed Hilmi and dated to 1012 Hegria. (1603 A.D.)

Reconstruction of the daily life of Antalya region nomad's centered around the black tent which is still in use today.

Nomad's Woolen Rug and Multi-colored Carrying Sack-Döşemealtı-Antalya.

- Woolen Rug
- Antalya/Döşemealtı, L:120 cm.W:90 cm.
- Beginning of 20th century. Inv.No: 1.31.75

Field with a halelli composition in pink, light yellowish green, blue, black, white and dark red on a red background. Main border decorated with kocasu, wide border. Thin borders composed of triangles, and camel motifs.

- Woolen Rug
- Antalya/Döşemealtı,L:177cm. W:114cm.
- 20th century. Inv.No: 1.20.74

Two niches, performing a hexagon, decorated with three cross-shaped motifs, locally called balls, four hoofed flowers and two balls of myrtle leaves. Spandrels ornamented with heybe suyu motifs. Borders composed of tutmaç, oleander; kocasu, wide border; and çingilli aksu.

An 18th-19th Century House in Antalya

A reconstruction of the interior of a typical 18th-19th century house in Antalya. Ceiling, carved doors, curtains, sheets and coverlets in the living room, bedroom and bathroom are original.

- Two Handled Copper Brazier
- D:106 cm. H:34 cm.
- 19th century- Antalya

HALL NUMBER XIII

In this hall the visitor is presented with a typical nineteenth century Antalya home with its living room, bedroom, and bathroom. These rooms generally project beyond the ground floor and have windows overlooking the street. Wooden ceilings are the common decorated parts, mostly for all rooms. These are made in a simple corbelling technique, are embellished with a little carving, a surrounding border or a central medallion.

The furniture in all living rooms is almost the same. The fireplace, cupboards and small niches providing decorative interest were the common elements of the room. Wooden divans are placed along the entire length of the windowed walls. A brazier at the centre of the room, a clock leaning against a wall and rugs and carpets spread on the floor complete the furnishing.

In another part of this hall there are samples of rugs chosen from the famous carpet centers of Anatolia, like Uşak, Gördes, Ladik, Mucur, Kula, Avanos and Bergama. Among the rugs on display is a sixteenth century Uşak "madallion" rug, the oldest and the largest rug of the museum's collection.

On the corridor leading the visitor out, various wood carvings employed in the homes of Antalya are displayed.

- Wooden Ceiling
- Antalya/Kaleiçi, L:435 cm. W:250 cm.
- 19th century. Inv.No: 76

Ceiling composed of a rhombus placed in a hexagon. Rhombus decorated with arabesque motifs around a rosette from small rhombuses. Blistered spandrels decorated with appliques in the form of meanders. Middle border, ornamented with intersecting circles and flanked by borders furnished with floral motifs.

NOTES